To companionshi

The Tears

The English Translation of
Al-Abarat
By Mustafa Lutfi Al-Manfaluti

Translated by

Majid Khan Malik Saddiqui

The Tears, The English Translation of Al-Abarat

Mustafa Lutfi Al-Manfaluti; Translated by Majid Khan Malik Saddiqui.

Copyright © 2017. Majid Khan Malik. All rights reserved. Edition 1. Published on the 26th June 2017.

ISBN 978-0-9930730-1-4

British Library Cataloguing in Publication Data.

A catalogue record for this book is available from the British Library.

Cover Design by Raheesa Malik – raheesamalik98@hotmail.com

Published by: Noor Alam publications

Malik Cloth House

122–126 Lumb lane

Bradford/ West Yorkshire/ BD8 7RS/UK

07969608551

majidmalik@hotmail.co.uk

www.hajisclothhouse.co.uk

Acknowledgments

I begin in the name of God. Peace and Blessings be upon the Prophet of Islam and all related Prophets before him.

This book *The Tears* is the English Translation of *Al-Abarat*, authored by Mustafa Lutfi Al-Manfaluti and translated by Majid Khan Malik Saddiqui. It has been compiled under the guidance of renowned Islamic Scholar and profound leader of the Naqshbandi Sufi Order;

Hazrat Allama Pir Alauddin Siddiqui Late (1936-2017)

My spiritual mentor and guide, without whom this work would not have existed.

We thank Allama Qazi Sajid Zafar, Allama Shawal Hashmi, Sobea Hussain, Umme Abid, Hamza Rahim Ali, Shafiqur Rahman, Amjad Bashir, Imran Iqbal, Wasim Akram, Nafisa Malik, Farhana Malik, Shamim Ara, Bilal Majid, Usman Hamid, Raheesa Malik and others who supported and proofread this project. Sincere thanks to my parents, Abdul Malik and Kalsoom Bi, also to my siblings and loved ones.

Context

Al-Abarat was first published in 1915 in Arabic in Egypt. The author Al-Manfaluti, was one of the greatest writers/novelists of his time. He was predominantly known for translating many plays and French novels into the Arabic language and authored many other works.

Al-Abarat includes eight short stories. Four of which are the author's own, and the other four are the translations and works of other writers, such as Chateavbriand, and Alexandre Dumas Fils.

All attempts have been made in order to accurately translate this classical Arabic into English. However, a direct word to word translation has not been carried out, because the formalities and conventions of the English language differ from the Arabic language. Certain vocabulary has been substituted to aid consistency and ease of understanding.

This book is also available as an EBook, ISBN: - 978-0-9930730-2-1. Also there is an extended version of this book available in hardback, including the Arabic text, extra reading about the author, Arabic transcription notes and acknowledgments in detail, making it practical for the academics. The Islamic name of God and its Prophet have been used in that book and not in this book, safeguarding and sanctifying their esteem. The ISBN of this book is: - 978-0-9930730-3-8

Author's note: -

This book has been read over exhaustively and checked limitless times. All efforts and scrutiny have been used to ensure that this book is free from any errors, discrepancies and deficiencies. However, as a reader or critic, if you do find a mistake, we would be grateful if you could point out the faults, so we can remove or rectify them in the next edition. To do this, please email - majidmalik@hotmail.co.uk

The Contents Page

*"**R**emember us, for we too have lived, loved and laughed."*

*(Quote taken from; **Shutter Island, 19/12/10 Hollywood Motion Picture. A closes up shot of the Hospital Cemetery stating this quote on a plaque**).*

THE ORPHAN

Some time ago, in a neighbouring high flat, there lived a boy, who was aged between nineteen or twenty. I presumed that he was a student, from the town's college or university.

I used to observe him regularly, through the window of my library, which was directly opposite his flat. Before me, I witnessed a paled faced, distressed and weak young man, sitting soulfully besides a kindled lamp in one corner of his room.

Sometimes, the young man was studying a book, or writing, at other times he was revising from a piece of paper. I never had paid attention or was bothered with a thing from his affairs until the night I returned to my house after midnight. The night was extremely cold. It was one of cold nights of the winter. I entered my library to work. I took a look at that young man and caught him sitting in his place besides his lamp. He was leaning with his head facing down upon the opened book before him. I presumed that he was either suffering from being awake or tiredness from revising. His eyes were heavy under the weight of sleep. Finally retiring for the night, while going to his bed, he fell down.

Before I had moved from my place, the young man raised his head and I discovered that his eyes were full of tears. He was weeping upon his book, tears had soaked the pages and erased the text, making the ink spread across the pages. After a while that young man gathered himself together, cleaned his pen and returned to his former state of studying.

It distressed me that I had seen this troubled, poor young man, who was all alone in a cold empty room in the dark night. He did not have a blanket or a fire which could protect him from the bitter coldness. He was grieving over the stresses of life, or he had fallen into the calamities of life before he had reached the age of stresses and calamities. He was in such a state, and had no one to share his feelings to, nor any helper. I thought to myself, that most certainly there must be a man with a broken heart behind this distressing scene, who's heart was rapidly melting away between his ribs, and his body was going to collapse like the way a deteriorated building would collapse. I stayed standing in my place, not moving until I saw him folding away his book and taken refuge in his bed. Then, I turned towards my bedroom.

The night passed with the exception of a little remaining. Only a small portion of darkness remained on the page of the horizon, near where the tongue of the morning would advance and lick it off.

After that, I continued to look at him during most nights. Either he was crying, or leaning forward, hitting his head on his chest. Sometimes he was wrapped up in bed sobbing like a distressed mother, who has lost her child, or walking up and down his room touching the walls in a distressed state until tiredness took over him. Then he would fall down on his chair, crying and screaming. I became emotionally moved and cried when I saw him cry, wishing I had the power to remove his calamities like a true friend. I wanted to discover his secret, so that I could participate in his sorrows. However, I disliked interfering, to discover the hidden secret of his heart as this would invade his privacy.

Yesterday, after a slight portion of the night had passed, I saw that his silent room was darkened. Initially I presumed that he had gone out for some matter, but after a while I heard from the midst of the room a constant low sound of wailing. I became worried, as I felt his calling came out from the bottom of his heart. I thought that this young man is ill, and does not have anyone who could care for him. I became increasingly concerned for his wretched state, and went to check on him.

My servant guided me with his lamp until I reached his house. Upon reaching the front door, I felt a dreadful fear, like one who is standing upon the door of a grave, to say his last farewell to its resident.

I entered and he opened his eyes when he felt my presence. In the dim lamp light, I saw the dazed look of amazement on his face. He stared at me for a while without talking and neither moving. I drew near to his bed and sat down next to him, declaring "I am your neighbour. For a while I have been listening to you, and have gathered that you require prompt medical attention. I know you are alone in this room. Are you ill? I am sorry for your condition and have come to help you as best as I can." He raised his hand slowly and placed it on his forehead, I too placed my hand on his head on top and I felt he was extremely and feverish.

His fever seemed to have passed through his body. He writhed and struggled in his loose leather shirt. I instructed my servant to bring the appropriate medicine from my home, and gave him a few drops.

Upon drinking, he regained some consciousness and said "Thank you" with the same look of amazement.

I asked "What is your pain O brother?"

He replied "I have no problem."

I then asked "How long have you been in this sorrowful state?"

He replied "I do not know."

I said "Do you require a doctor? Can I call him for you so that he may examine you?"

He let out a long sigh, looked at me sadly and said "Verily the one who gives preference to life over death is the one who needs a doctor." Then he closed his eyes and returned to his unconscious state.

I did not have any other alternative but to call a doctor, whether he wanted one or not. I sent for him, and he arrived in an angered state, complaining and sighing loudly because I had disturbed his bedrest I made him come through small, dark alleyways on a cold night. I apologized, but did not care about his complaints as I would pay him well. He felt the pulse of the patient and whispered in my ear "O sir your patient is hovering upon danger, I am presuming that he will not stay alive for much longer, only God knows and we do not know." He sat in a corner and began to write a prescription and his bill. Satisfied with my apologies, he then left. I brought the prescribed medicine and spent the entire night on the patient's side, like the way a lost star in the night of the sky. I continued his medication throughout the night, and cried for his wretched state until the early hours of the morning.

He gained consciousness, and turned his eyes around his bed until he saw me, asking "Are you still here?"

I replied "Yes, and I hope that you are feeling better than before."

He sighed "If only I hoped that was the case."

I asked "Dear brother, can I ask who you are? Why are you alone in this house? Are you a stranger in this town, or are you from its residents? Are you suffering from a physical illness, or an internal pain?"

He replied "I am suffering both."

I said "Could you tell me about your condition and your pain, the way a friend opens up to a friend? I have become concerned for you."

He said, "Do you promise me to hide my secret if God grants me life, and safeguard my will if I die?"

I replied "Yes."

He said "I have trusted your promise, because the one who holds a heart as honourable as yours, could not be a liar nor a deceiver. I am the son of so and so, my father passed away a very long time ago, leaving me poor and alone at the age of six. I had no wealth so my paternal uncle took guardianship of me. He was the most noble from all uncles, extremely good and kind, the best in love and generosity. He loved me as much as he loved his small daughter. She was my age or a little younger than me. It gave him great happiness to see by her side a brother, which he had wished from God for a very long time.

Hence he favoured me the way he favoured her. He enrolled us to school on the same day. I loved my new sister very much. I found happiness and memorable moments in her companionship, which took away my problems and the pain of losing my parents. People would always see us both going to school or returning, playing in the porch or the garden. We used to be studying in the library or talking to one another in the bedroom, until she came of age, wore a veil and stayed indoors. I continued with my studies in the outside world.

Our hearts became knotted in a timeless love. I only found the taste of life in her company and the light of chastity in the morning of her smiles. I would have gladly sacrificed all the happiness in the world for each moment I spent with her. She was a young lady of great calibre, chastity, forbearance, mercy, purity and humility.

Our happy childhood days were the great white wings which shaded and distanced me from my earlier darkness, sorrows and the calamities. Our souls sparkled like sparkling drinks in tall glasses.

I can still see that flowered garden which inhabited our happiness, dreams and wishes, as if it is in front of me, with its water shining and pebbles glittering. Branches and multi-coloured flowers radiated a beautiful fragrance, as we both sat on the bench in the morning and evening, passing the time in merriment and delightful discussions. Sometimes we would prepare a bouquet of flowers, muse over the pages of a book, even compete with one another in drawing. I clearly remember the low-lying green bushes, under which we would peacefully rest after we had raced and become tired, like baby chicks find security in the comfort of their mother's wings.

I can remember that we used sticks to make small holes in the ground, which we declared as the edges of canals and reservoirs. We would fill them up with water and sit around pretending to fish, even putting the fish in the water ourselves. The moment we used to capture a fish, we were overwhelmed by happiness, as if we had captured some great booty. I still remember the strange golden cages in which we used to raise sparrows and different kind of birds, enjoying their company for long periods. They brought us great joy, and we named them and cared for them, watching them drink water and peck seeds. When we called them, they would respond by whistling and chirping.

In reality, I had become unsure whether my love was merely brotherly or a lover's infatuation. However, what I did know very clearly was that our love was doomed, as I had withheld my feelings, and never told her that I loved her. This was because she was my uncle's daughter and my childhood friend. So, how could I be the one to hurt her feelings? Also I did not have the nerve nor the power to join our lives as one. I knew that her parents would not approve of the likes of me, a poor person of straitened circumstances, as suitable match for their daughter's marriage and welfare. I always considered her superior to me and never wanted to be embarrassed in this way before her. Furthermore, I never dwelled into the secrets of her heart, and clarify whether she loved me as a brother or as a lover. If it was the latter, then I might even have pressed her parents for their daughter's hand. However, the reality of my love for her was like that of a secluded priest, who in a church worships the statue of virgin Mary and does not look at her with any wrong intention.

We both continued living our innocent lives, until my uncle became extremely ill. Unable to recover he left this world as God claimed his soul. On his death bed, he declared in his last words to his wife that he had always loved me dearly and held me in high esteem. He requested her to continue my upbringing and nurturing, which death had not allowed him to complete. He also bid her to be like a loving and caring mother to me just like he had been a loving and caring father. This way, I would not suffer from his loss.

The days of mourning were not even over yet, when I began to see the faces, eyes and circumstances changing. Before this, I had never encountered such animosity in my uncle's house. I was grieved, and felt at despair from life. For the first time ever, I felt like a stranger in the household, despised and rejected.

One morning, when I was sitting in my room, the house maid entered: She was an extremely chaste and a sincere woman and discreetly said 'The Lady (my aunt) has a request. She would like to get her daughter married soon as she has no father now, and it is inappropriate for you both to stay together like this, now you are adults. Your current life together will send wrong connotations to her future fiancé. Consequently, she would like you to move out, so she can turn your room into an abode for the new couple. All your requirements will be taken care of, you will not even feel that you have separated.'

I felt like the maiden had stuck a sharp arrow in my liver. Quickly composing I said, 'Very soon with the will of God I will do just that, I accept this decision.' When she had left, I shed a stream of tears in loneliness. To leave this house now was the decree of God the Almighty.

When the night-fall came, I packed my bag with my clothes and books. My heart was heavy. All the fortunes of life rested with the one I loved, through her I had learned also to love myself. There was now a veil between us, so I had no regrets after this. I sneaked out from the house very quietly so no one would find out. Before I departed, I took one last look at my uncle's daughter behind the curtain: She was sleeping. This the last time I ever set eyes on her.

I swear by your life, I did not leave Baghdad in happiness.

Only if I could have found an alternative way not to leave.

How grievous it was, that I did not have the power to say my farewells.

And I was unable to speak to its loving residents.

Like this, I parted from the house which I had spent many happy days, similar to the way Prophet Adam (Peace and blessings of God be upon him) was taken out from Paradise. I was surprised, despised and afflicted with love. Sorrows and hardships were hovering upon me once again. Knowing also that I would be separated from my childhood companion, I was destitute with no authority or friend. I entered poverty and found no well-wisher or helper from amongst the people.

Despite everything, I had some money remaining from the good times which were long gone. With it, I rented this room, as I did not have the power to stay at my old residence even for a moment. I intended to journey the open land belonging to God, so that I could cure myself from the tribulations and afflictions which had befallen me. I undertook a long journey for several months, traveling from one city to the other, spending sunrise somewhere and sunset somewhere else. Finally, my heart gained peace when my tears rested in my eye sockets, neither had they shed nor did they become dry.

I became content with my lot. The school's annual term was commencing soon, so I returned. I solemnly pledged to live alone on this earth, even if I am in a community, I will be absent from its affairs and dealings. I will forget everything other than my love, and seek the power to continue my life without her. Thus, I became bound to my room and my school, and I never parted from them. Time helped me to conceal all traces of her memory. Rarely when my past did resurface, I shed a few tears for her, but revealed nothing to anyone. Only God knew of my pain, and this fact cooled my heart.

Stubbornly I remained in this state until yesterday, when I directed my attention to my remaining money and I saw that soon it would be expire. In order to continue with life and also to pay for my schooling, these funds were crucial. In this city, schools are very expensive workshops, which do not give credit. Knowledge is an asset only for the rich, acquired through wealth. No one is ready to bestow knowledge for free.

This troubled me as I could not see any means to acquire my livelihood. In desperation, I took all my extra books to the book market. Despite spending all day there, I found no one who was even ready to give a quarter of the price of the books. I left in despair, despising my unfortunate luck.

When I arrived home, at the door step, I saw a woman who was enquiring about me from the residents. When I took a closer look at her I realised that she was the maid from my uncle's house who used to take care of me.

'You?' I asked.

She replied, 'Yes.'

I enquired 'What brings you here?'

She answered 'If you permit me I would like to speak to you.'

I took her to my room, when we were alone I requested her 'Now tell me.'

She said, 'It has been three days since I have been finding you but I could not seek your address, finally I have located you.'

After this, she burst out crying loudly. Her crying troubled me, and I feared some calamity had befallen upon the house which I had loved so dearly. I asked 'Why are you crying?'

She replied, 'Do you not know anything about your uncle's house?'

I said 'No, what is the matter?'

She moved her hand towards her veil and from it she took out an enveloped letter. I took the letter from her and slit off its seal, knowing immediately it was from my cousin, my uncle's daughter. The words imprinted on it are seared in my memory until this day. It read,

'You parted from me, without even saying goodbye, but I still forgive you. Now I have reached the door of my grave. If you do not come now, I will never forgive you. Are you not going to come to me for the last time to say your farewells?'

I threw the letter from my hands and advanced towards the door rapidly. The maid restrained me and asked 'Where are you going?'

I said 'She is ill and I have to be with her, it is important.'

For a moment, she became silent and motionless, and in a trembling low voice said 'You do not need to do so, dear. Before you get to her, you will discover that she has already passed away, and has met her Lord.'

When I heard this, it felt like that my heart had moved from its place to another. The earth started spinning, in a daze I fell down to the ground, having no sense of what was happening around me. I gained consciousness after a long time. When I opened my eyes, I discovered it was night. I saw the maid sitting beside me screaming and crying. I drew closer to her and asked her, 'O woman. Is it true what you say?'

She replied 'Yes.'

I requested 'Tell me everything.' She began...

'O sir, verily your uncle's daughter, could not contain her grief after you left. She enquired after the reason for your departure. I had told her about that message which your aunty instructed me to convey. To this her only reply was 'What will happen to him now? A poor man in such dire circumstances?! They do not know anything about me and him.' After this, she never spoke of you again, either good or bad. Nevertheless, news of your departure seared her heart deeply, and she endured the terrible pain in silence for a few days, until she became ill. Her beauty withered, and her smile dried up. She became bed bound and worsened still. Her mother became fearful for her health. She stopped discussing marriages and grooms with her in case she grew worse, despite it being the only subject she seemed to revel in day and night. In her desperation to cure her daughter, she consulted every doctor and herbalist, but no one could do anything for her, as she slowly and gradually headed towards her grave.

It was during this time that I stayed awake for a few nights at her bedside. She gestured me to move closer, so promptly I drew near to her. She indicated that I hold her hand. I did so, and helped her to sit upright. Weakly she asked me, 'What part of the night are we in?'

I replied 'A small portion of the night still remains.'

She asked, 'Are you alone here?'

I replied, 'Yes, all the people of this house are sleeping.'

She enquired 'Do you know the abode of my cousin?'

I was surprised by her question, as I had never before heard from her tongue anything relating to this matter. I replied, 'Certainly dear, I know of his place.' Even though I had no idea of it. I felt sorry for her, and desired that the last remaining thread of hope which she had of finding you, did not break.

Then she said to me 'Are you going to help me by delivering my letter to him?'

I replied, 'My respectable Lady, I will love to do this.'

Again through her gestures she indicated that the ink pot be brought to her. I did so, and with it she wrote the letter which you have just read.

When morning commenced, I left the house, enquiring your address from one place to the other. I was observing faces of people passing by, hoping that I may see you or that I may find one who may guide me to you. Despite all my efforts, I was unsuccessful. As the sun set, I returned home, finding that some part of the night had already passed: Fearfully I heard mourning and crying, and sadly realised that the arrow of death had hit its mark once again. Our home had lost its rose, the fresh rose which used to bless this world with its beauty. Its last petal had just fallen. I was grieving like the way a mother would grieve for the death of her only child. Other than this day, I had never before witnessed a day of such grief and bereavement.

The greatest sadness for me was the fact that she wanted to see you in her last moments of life, but was unfortunate not to do so. She passed away before she could be granted her wish. After her death, I secretly safeguarded her letter and continued to look for you until this day.'

I thanked her for this favour, and permitted her request to leave my home. When I was left alone, I felt that a black cloud was rising steadily towards my eyes until everything in front of me was hidden. I do not remember anything after until I saw you."

He stopped talking and took a warm breath. Through his sighs I felt that his liver was coming out piece by piece. I drew near him and asked him, "What has happened to you?"

He replied, "I want to shed a tear so that I can lessen my sorrow but I am unable to do so."

For a while he remained in silence. I felt that he was whispering something. When I listened closely, I discovered, he was saying,

"O God, you know that I am a traveller upon this earth: I have no one who can take care of me, nor any helper. I am a dependant, I am not the owner of the necessities of life. I cannot help myself. I am helpless and weak. I do not see a way towards any door from the doors of livelihood and neither am I capable of devising a plan for my welfare. Certainly the wound which has afflicted me, has ground my heart to pieces. Thus, nothing remains from it other than the ruins of my spirit. Verily I feel shame when I take my hands towards my soul, which you have placed with your hands. I want to strip it out from its place and throw it in your courts, so that you are disappointed with it and be ready to punish it. Therefore, command my soul back to you. Take back your possession and call it towards your pure house. No doubt, the best house is your house and the best neighbours are your neighbours."

Then he held his head with his hand as if he was stopping it from escaping. In a weak silent voice, he said, "My head is burning severely and my heart is melting away. I guess that I will not remain for long upon this wretched earth." In these final moments, he turned to me in desperation, imploring "If God grants me death like He did to her, please promise to place my grave next to hers, and also bury this letter with me."

I replied "Yes but I pray to God for your speedy recovery and health."

He said "Now I can die peacefully, not worrying about a thing." Then he took one shivering fit and died.

***

No doubt, I severely grieved the death of this troubled young man. I had the power to fulfil his dying wish, and buried him with his cousin and the letter also. Her letter had called him, and he could only respond to her through his death.

In this way, two loyal friends were united. The world and castle above them had become too tight to accommodate their love and companionship. Despite this, after their death, the ditches of their grave had created enough space to contain them both, finally sealing their union.

THE MARTYRS

After the death of her husband and her parents, nothing remained for her, other than her small son whom she loved, and a caring brother. She also had a little wealth, with which it she could pass by the remaining days of her life.

However now, that remaining wealth had also come to pass. Her brother had been afflicted by the harmful events of society, the society had snatched away his wealth and everything. Due to this, he had left and went far away, and his whereabouts were unknown. After this, she had become needy and support less.

This unfortunate woman went through so much pain and so many tribulations, which hardly any mankind could bear, in search for livelihood. She stitched clothes until her eyesight became extremely weak, she washed so many clothes that her hands became dry. She made so many trips to the factories until she became helpless. Nevertheless, she and her son managed to stay alive.

A woman like this should not be permitted to live. However, God favoured her by taking away her prosperity and equipped her with the wealth of patience. Thus, when the night of misfortunes unlit her surroundings and her life darkened in front of her, then far in the horizon, she used to see an outburst of three rays due to the mercy of God. Hence, these three rays used to penetrate in her heart which then filled her with patience and peace. One ray was of the love that she had for her son, the other ray was of the hope that she had of her brother returning, and the third ray was of the happiness that her self-respect and dignity was still safeguarded.

The days kept passing by conventionally, eventually she grew old and her son became a young adult. The pain of hardship transported from her heart into the young man's heart. Now it was crucial for him to stay alive in order to think of the welfare of his mother like the way she had always thought of the welfare of her son. Hence, he embarked on a search for his livelihood at all roads, and stopped at every spring in search for provisions. Eventually luck took him towards the faculty of painting/drawing. He became content with this profession, and gave his full attention towards it. As time went on, he mastered this art.

However, time does not highlight the qualities of a person, it is the person himself who through his wisdom and understanding highlights his qualities. Unfortunately, this young man did not possess this attribute and neither did he know of a way to promote himself, therefore he was left unknown. Through this profession, he gained his provision, drop by drop. Although for his mother, he could not give her complete prosperity, he by all means, was able to obtain the essentials and the necessities of life. Thus, his mother sufficed upon this and started to stay at home as she felt the coolness of tranquillity in her heart.

However, when she remembered her separated brother, she longed for him like the way an old mother cow yearns for its lost calf. She was highly grieved over the fact that she had not seen him for fifteen years and that no letter had come from him. Since ten years till this day, she had no place of refuge where she could take her pain and sorrows to. She used to cry in seclusion until her grief was satisfied, then she used to come out to greet her son in a jovial state of happiness as if she had not cried before.

One day her son entered her room when she was alone. Thus, he saw her crying while she was holding a picture in her hand. When he observed the picture closely, he discovered that it was the picture of his maternal uncle. At that point he felt that hidden pain in his mother's heart and he withheld his flowing tears in his lashes. It was very difficult for him to control his emotions. He advanced towards his mother and placed his hand upon her shoulder and said "O mother, just have a little more patience, soon you will find out about your lost brother."

Her face out of happiness began to twinkle and she said "How is that?"

He said "It has come to my attention, that after a few months in Washington, which is the capital of America, there is going to be an Art exhibition in which there have allocated small and big prizes for the contestants. One of my friends has promised me that he will help me with the travel expenses, so that perhaps I may become recognised through this Art exhibition, and can save myself and you from this unfortunate life of calamity and hardship. Over there I will search for your lost brother. I will keep on searching for him until I find him or obtain convincing and definite news about him."

Her twinkling face drooped and she said "O son do not do this, because by seeing you besides me, I do not find myself to be unfortunate, and neither are you unfortunate. Are you not content with the distribution of God? If you were to do this, then upon the face of the earth there would not be a more sorrowful and unfortunate woman than me. If I have cried once for my brother, then upon your separation I will cry a thousand times. Whenever I remember him, I take a look at your face in which I then find patience and peace. So how can I possibly gain patience if both of you be away from my eyes?"

Despite her reluctance, he kept on persuading her, kept on urging, until finally he had convinced her. She became tender and agreed to entrust his affair with God.

After a few days, destiny struck with adversities. The mother was left all alone in France without a friend and neither a helper. Her son became a stranger, helpless and without any support in America.

The young man managed to reach the Art exhibition and presented his pictures. Amongst them was a drawing of the shore and the ocean where his mother was saying her farewells. This was an extremely emotional sight, and very beautifully sketched. People were highly impressed with it and liked it a great deal. They agreed to fix a prize for his efforts the way he had been expecting. When that prize reached his hands, he felt that he was one of the greatest people on the face of this Earth. This was his first day where he had been recognised. It was as if before this moment, he had never tasted the bitterness of life and neither had he seen the face of calamities.

Like this, life plays with a human being, and it makes him taste the flavours of both joy and adversity. It makes a person face different hardships and difficulties until he is desolate and doubtful. At that point his heart becomes full of rage and anger. After that, life sparkles a false hope of light in the dark sky, then with his free will and pleasure, man returns to his abode like a non-understanding animal heading towards his place of slaughter with the greed of eating grass and hay. How man, through the hands of life, can become fortunate and likewise unfortunate?

That young man sent some money to his mother and kept some for himself. He wrote to his mother saying, 'Until I do not fulfil my promise I will remain here.' He progressed in search for his maternal uncle from one town to the other. He enquired about him from every resident and every immigrant he met. He finally met someone who told him that his last meeting with his uncle was a couple of years ago. He told him that his uncle was in the process of embarking upon an expedition towards the southern islands in search of brass mines. As soon as he heard this, he commenced his journey towards where he was told, in order to get to his maternal uncle.

He finally reached a wasted land, an island which was extremely frightful. Its towns were still shadowed with the old dark traditions and customs. He passed by a Negro tribe who dwelled behind an isolated mountain. When they saw him, hatred and enmity arose within their hearts against him, and their animosity against white people awoke. They even hated the shining sun and the lighted stars. Thus, they had surrounded him, raided him and then arrested him and took him towards their dwelling. Over there they detained him in an underground tunnel, they used to call this the prison of retribution.

***

Here, he realised that the fortune, prosperity and hope sparkling in the sky on the day of the exhibition, was nothing other than the deception of life. The happiness which he had thought to be his future destiny, perished yesterday, and he had become the corroded pages of an old manuscript.

He had the ability to overcome the hardship which he had fallen into, and bear his suffering. However, one adversity which was too heavy and difficult for him, was that another soul was participating in his misfortune. His shoulders were burdened with the problems and responsibility of his mother.

They descended him into a prison cell and tied him up with a heavy chain with enormous links. Then they closed the door on him, leaving him all alone. In his loneliness, he opened his eyes, and could not see anything in front of him. He was not able to distinguish whether he had become blind, or whether he was in pitch black darkness, which hid everything from his eyes. He, himself was in the state of shock until the night had elapsed, and through a small crack from the wall of the prison cell, he saw a small ray of the sun entering as a thin thread of whiteness. He stood before this stranger and became attached to it, like a traveller becomes attached to his companion. He thanked the sun which had sent him a messenger to console him in his loneliness. His eyes continued following that sun beam as if dependent upon it. Wherever that sunbeam went, his eyes shifted towards it. Eventually, he could see, that ray of sun shrinking and gradually departing. Then it ascended back from that crack within the wall where it had descended from and went back to the sky where it had come from. He grieved its separation and parting the way a loyal friend feels pain when he is separated from his companion.

He looked around his surroundings and discovered that the pieces of darkness were gathering around him and that they were merging into one another. He realised that he was also a dark fragment from the fragments of darkness which were turning in on him. He was disturbed, perplexed like the spirit is within the darkness of the grave. He did not know of his whereabouts or location.

He began to walk in that tight space, touching with his hand, struggling to find himself, until he heard the sound of the chain which was cuffed to his feet, and found himself. He was tired from walking. Thus, he fell down crying.

Like this, the connection of this poor man was cut-off from the rest of the world. There remained no link good or bad, for this man and the outside world, other than that bright sunbeam which used to come every morning in order to greet him, or that gatekeeper who used to knock on his door every evening.

Not even a complete year had passed. As that man had forgotten himself, he forgot his mother and had forgotten the world that he lived in along with the world that he was currently in. He forgot the day and the night. He failed to distinguish darkness from light. He also failed to acknowledge fortunes from misfortunes. He was standing upon the edge of life and death. He was neither happy nor sad. He did not remember the past and had no hope for the future. He did not know whether in between the nearby stones there was a stone, a fragment of darkness, a moving body, an imagination, a superstition or only a mere non-existing entity.

***

A few years had passed by upon his poor and helpless mother who did not see her son and neither did she find anyone who could direct her towards him. People used to see her on the streets; an old, lost, hunched-back lady who was passionately in love with her son, mourning his separation. In her hand there was a walking stick, with it she walked, and it swivelled in her hand. Her skinny and bent body had torn rags hanging off her. An observer could only speculate that due to them being extremely old, they were pieces of cloth which were dangling from her, or either they were rotten old clothes which the wind was pushing through the air.

Every morning she used to visit places of worship, going to go to the doors of churches, synagogues and mosques in order to beg God for mercy. She asked food from passers-by. When the sun used to set from the heart of the sky, she walked towards the sea shore and sat on one of the rocks, whispering to the waves and to the particles of sand. She used to look at the circular horizon very carefully, like a fortune-teller would observe the stars in the sky with scrutiny. Whenever there was a gust of breeze in her direction she used to sense the fragrance of her son. Whenever she saw a wave coming in her direction, she acknowledged that it was a message from her son.

Whenever she saw a ship on the surface of the ocean, she presumed that it was that ship which was bringing back her son. Her eyes used to rest upon it, until the ship's anchor was casted. She stood in the paths of the passengers, identifying them and very closely monitoring their behaviour and screaming her son's name as loud as possible. She stood saying "O the people of God, who can tell me about my son? Who can find him for me on the face of this earth? I have lost him a long time ago, after him the world has afflicted me with calamities, I cannot forget him nor can I find him in any possible way." She continued saying "At least through guesswork, for the sake of God, please tell me, has he returned with you or was he unable to come with you? Is he going to come after you, or has the world finished him off so that after today, I keep no hope of him returning?" Not even a single soul paid any attention to her, nor could they understand her plea. Very rarely if anyone did pay any attention to her, they presumed that she was insane, and out of pity and compassion for her they gave her some money.

She remained in this state and station, until she saw the mothers, sisters and young ladies departing towards their houses with their children, brothers and fathers. The people passing by the sea shore had gone, and that other than her there was no one remaining. She then took her walking stick and with the aid of it, came home slowly.

Now she used to spend her time next to the corner of a grave which she dug in the ground with her own hands, calling it her son's grave. Most times she used to cry over it and murmur over it. She used to say "O my son, which land has taken you in its bosom? Where is your abode? Under which star was your place of death? Where is your place of residence in the ocean? In which wild-cattle's stomach is your dwelling? If that bird who tore up your intestines, or that wild-cattle who stained its paws with your blood, or that grave which has hidden you inside itself, or that ocean which has took you in its belly only knew, that behind you there is an old, poor and a helpless mother which is going to cry over you, then certainly they would have been compassionate towards you because of me.

O son please come back, whether you are poor, disabled or even blind, for me it is sufficient enough that whenever I depart from this world, I can give you a last farewell kiss. And I will take a pledge from you to visit my grave day and night, so that through your visits, any hardships of the grave become light for me. Through your radiant face becomes illuminated that extreme darkness. How fortunate and lucky are those mothers who go to their graves before their children and how unfortunate are those mothers whose children go to their graves first. However, the most unfortunate and helpless mother is that one who is slowly crawling towards her death and she does not know whether she has left her son behind or that she will find him in the next life."

Like this, her state remained from morning to night. She used to cry over her son like how Prophet Jacob used to cry over his son (Prophet Joseph), until, like Prophet Jacob her sight had perished, but she still could not endure having patience and hope for her son's return. (Peace and blessings of God be upon all the Prophets).

***

One night, the prison guard came close to the young man, he drew his hands towards the chain which was connected to the wall and pulled it towards himself. The prisoner did not say anything to him nor did he even speculate in his heart that today may be the time of his release or whether it was the time of his death. The gatekeeper brought him out from the prison cell and fastened his chain to a rock which was near the central meeting place for the tribal villagers. After the gatekeeper had done this, he left.

The man then opened his eyes and discovered his location was changed. He learned that he had entered into another setting than his previous scene. He acknowledged that he was under a different sky and on top of another land. His senses were slowly and gradually coming back to him until he gained full awareness. He began to ponder and familiarise himself with his surroundings.

Here, he remembered the fortunes and the misfortunes of his migration and his home land. He recollected the prison cell, the darkness within and those chains along with their weight. Then his memories powered through, and, crossing the ocean, he remembered his mother. His lengthy departure would surely have afflicted her with unimaginable grief. Her separation was terrible for him. During this recollection, his eyes shed one tear, this was the first tear which he shed from the dark times of his adversities. From then onwards, he cried and cried uncontrollably until one portion of the night had passed. All the people went to their abodes and slept on their beds peacefully. He inclined his head upon his knees and allowed his thoughts to travel wherever he had pleased for them to go.

He was in such a state that tiredness and sleep was hovering upon his eyes. At once, he felt the touch of a hand upon his shoulder. He raised his head and saw a bright and a white body standing before him. He thought that it was a shining angel who had descended from the highest points of the skies in order to save him from his hardships. When he observed closely, he realised that it was a very beautiful, white, young lady, who he never seen before. In her whiteness, there was a very fine brownish colour mixed with it, like fine, brownish, wheat coloured cloud, which is mixed with the sunlight at forenoon.

He asked her "Who are you?"

She replied "I am a girl belonging to this tribe, I felt sorry for you seeing you in this state. Learning that you are an unfortunate man, I have come over to sympathise with you and to release you from your shackle so that you become free and go wherever you please. On the Day of Judgment, a person cannot offer a bigger gift to his Lord other than showing that he has counselled and helped a troubled person, and removed his worldly calamities."

The man was amazed that a pagan and a barbaric white Negro woman, would have so much love and affection in her heart for the troubled and hopeless. He presumed in his heart that certainly there must have been some catastrophe that she had gone through. He pondered upon this excessively, and her love upon his heart became firm. He forgot all of the affairs of life, with the exception of her, as only she remained in his thoughts.

For a short time, he remained silent and did not say anything, then he spoke "Dear Lady, please mind your way, I do not seek salvation." She realised that despair was gradually dominating him. She drew near him and put her hand on his shoulder and said,

"Do not give way to despair in your heart, O young man save your life from the hands of death, because there is no distance remaining between you and death. If you are still here when the veil upon the face of the night is removed, then the sharp edges of swords will slice your meat. Do not frighten your heart with the thought of death, neither grieve this sad, poor woman who is standing in front of you. I will be extremely saddened to see you slaughtered through the hands of a butcher, or become a morsel entering the mouths of people."

He said to her "You cannot release me."

She replied "I do not understand what you are talking about, because I know for what reason and why I have come here."

He said "Prior to this I was tied up in a bond. Now, you are the relationship which I am bound to. If you were to open the chains of my feet, how are you possibly going to open the bond of my heart?" She understood and realised what his heart contained.

In pain she raised her head towards the sky for a moment. Then he also raised his head towards her and observed her like how an artist would observe his masterpiece. He witnessed a warm tear drop flow from her eye and fall in front of him. Her tears fell heavily on his cheeks, a single tear rolled from his eye and met her tear, they mixed and became one.

He stretched out his hand towards her coverlet and pulled it towards himself saying, "O my respectable lady you have been standing up for a while now, please sit with me so that we may talk about things." She sat next to him as he said "At this stage, my tear joining with your tear means that, whether living or dead we will never part from one another. If you are intending to release me now, how possibly can I take freedom other than with you?"

She said "Only if I had the power to do that O dear."

He said "What is prohibiting you from doing this O lady?"

She looked at him with eyes full of tears and said "I fear that I will start loving you."

He said "And why would you fear?"

She said "I do not know."

He said "I will not ask you about that which you are hiding in your heart, however only a request which is to leave my affair in the hands of destiny, and let it decide for me. Verily I had feared death before I had met you, however now I am reassured that your glance of mercy will overcome the bitterness of death when you will look at my place of slaughter, and is sufficient for me that tear which you will drop on my grave after my death."

She welcomed his conversation. Her cheeks dampened with flowing tears, like scattered pearls from a broken necklace. Then, she advanced her hands towards the chains and broke them fiercely. She said "Come on, I will come with you, let the decree of God be in our favour."

Both of them set off, passing through jungles, crossing rivers and lakes, enduring the hot and cold weather, drinking sour and sweet water, eating dry and ripe fruits. When a shade of a tree, or a river bank approached, or if they saw a ravine, they rested for a while and then advanced. Ever since the girl had left her native country, a shade of bleakness had shown upon her face like the shade of a cloud which never dispersed.

Whenever they camped at a place they used to make their beds from its soil and its stones. Hence she used to get up from her sleep after resting for some night, and then she used to advance to some corner where she could not be found. There she used to place her hand on her chest and then she used to take out a small cross which she kissed and then mumbled some words. She used to behave in a strange manner, whispering to an invisible man and seeking forgiveness for her sins. From him, she used to seek help on her journey, for which the outcome was unknown. She remained on this state until dawn break. Then, she returned where she slept. Whenever the man wanted to enquire of her affair, she avoided it, and would stop him, until he felt shame asking her again. Thus he left her in her state. He himself was bearing and hiding such a big calamity in his heart, bigger than hers by many times.

After thirty days, the pair had drawn closer to some population. They were excited. At this point, they were convinced that they had left all their troubles and misfortunes behind them. Both of them came close to a small lake. On its bank, they sat under some thick trees and started talking. This was the first time they had indulged in conversation.

The young man said "See, how God safeguarded us in this long journey, which was through the barren and frightening jungle. God has done this, because He has written in the destiny, in the divine tablet for us a fortune. This is such a fortune that was not probably even prescribed for his pious people in Paradise."

She said "When has this life ever been an abode or a station of fortunes, and when has ever its residents been successful, that we may also become successful like them?" She continued to say "And if happiness in this life is difficult to obtain, then to find happiness, a human being should live satisfied with the belief that no one is happy in the world, only then can he pass his days of destiny peacefully and with satisfaction. This way, no false wish or hope can hinder his joy of life."

He said "Prosperity is in front of us, between it and us is only the distance of this desolate ground. If we wish to pass it, it should not be a big deal. We will take refuge in the first house, whichever one it should be from the houses of God. For a short while in front of the place of slaughter, we will bend down on our knees, then after that, we will come out as a flourishing couple as there will be no obstacle standing in between us and neither would a second environment be the means of unpleasantness."

For a moment the girl put her head down and then she raised it. On her cheek, a clear tear was rolling down. The young man said, "O dear why are you crying?"

She said "Do you remember the night of escape when you invited me to runoff with you, as I told you if I were to run away with you, I will fall in love with you."

He said "Yes."

The girl said "Woe! Today it has happened what I feared." Then she started to scream out aloud and said "O mother what have you done?" She fell down face front. The man drew near to her and held her in his arms. He saw that her body parts were shaking extremely and that she was feverish. So, he broke off some twigs from the tree in order to kindle a fire. From afar he saw a cottage.

In search of a spark to kindle the twigs, he advanced towards the cottage. When he had reached at the door of that small house, he met an old dignified priest. He offered the priest his greetings. The priest replied to his greetings in a very respectable manner and asked him "O son what is the matter?"

He replied "I have left a poor girl at the river bank who is shivering with cold. Do you have a spark, so that I could take it to light a fire?"

The priest gave him a spark and said "God has prescribed for you and for your patient wellbeing and good health. You carry on and I will follow behind you."

The young man ran fast until he reached the river bank. To his amazement he saw the girl sitting down comfortably. She was not complaining of any cold or pain. With a smile he approached her and said "As days are passing by, perhaps the pain of parting from your home and from your community is slowly but gradually departing."

In response she said "I have no such thing in my heart."

Then she said "Please sit down, I will tell you the entire story, because time has come now that I reveal my secret to you." He sat next to her.

She said "I am also a foreigner like you. I do not know anyone from these villages nor do I know this land. Other than myself, I only know about a grave whose signs have also perished and its resident decayed due to being buried for a long time. My mother gave me birth on a bed belonging to a man with white complexion. This man was from your end and came here about twenty years ago. He passed through here and met my mother. Both starting loving each other and ran away behind this desolated land. My mother had accepted his religion and then got married with him. Then they gave birth to me. For a term we lived a life of peace and prosperity.

The people belonging to my mother's tribe were always in search for us, until one dark night, they raided us. They took us all to their homeland and at that time I was close to turning ten years old. In front of me and my mother, they killed my father. That sight, I can still picture today and it still does not part from my vision. This extreme sadness started to draw my mother closer to her grave until her time also came. A devotee of Jesus Christ (Peace and blessings of God be upon him) at that time was present, whom sometimes used to come and go there. My mother had brought me in front of him and said to me 'O daughter, my mother had given me birth to face tribulations in this world, I fear that I have likewise given you birth for the same reason. It is sufficient for you that you also do not become a means of this misfortune after me, like virgin mother Mary (Peace and blessings of God be upon her) you also take a pledge of not marrying, which then only death can solve.' In front of the priest I accepted this order and made him a witness over this account. Then, after that, my mother's face starting sparkling with happiness and joy as then she raised her glance towards the sky and said 'O Roneal I am coming behind you' as her soul departed."

The young man, upon hearing this name, startled and said "Do you know about your father's country and his family?"

She said "Yes."

When she had clarified and explained it the young man jumped up in joy and said, "O God! Thank you, I have found my lost thing."

The girl was surprised and said "Which lost thing?"

The young man said "Do you remember the night we met, and our tears joined together and I said to you that our connection is unbreakable until death?

She replied "Yes."

He said, "Before this day I only loved you, now I am even closer to you. From today onwards you are my love and also my maternal uncle's daughter."

In a low voice she starting saying, "O God! Thank you, in this delicate moment I have found besides me a brother." Her body in a very severe state starting shaking and her face slowly but gradually started to become fatigued.

The young man become scared and inclined towards her and said "What am I seeing?"

She said "Do not be worried, put your ear next to me so that I can tell you my remaining story which you have not heard fully as yet." She continued her story saying, "Ever since I have safeguarded my mother's will and entrusted my life towards virgin mother Mary (Peace and blessings of God be upon her), now it was inevitable for me to find a place of refuge for that day when my temptations overpower my religion. For this reason, I have always kept this small glass bottle with me. Now that day has arrived which I had feared. I have taken refuge in this and I have entrusted you towards God."

The young man started to look at that direction which the girl had pointed to. He discovered that a bottle was placed behind him. He picked it up only to find that it was empty and that only a few yellow drops were remaining in its vessel. From there, he understood everything.

The young man felt as if a fragment of his heart had broken off and was trapped in his ribs, and as if a bird had spread out his wings and through his head, had flown away in the sky's atmosphere. Thus, he fell down in his state, unconscious. He did not feel anything around him after that. After a while, he gained consciousness and opened his eyes, only to find the girl besides him had become cold. He saw there standing in front of her the same priest from the cottage, holding food which he had brought for both of them in his hand. He was looking at her with a glance of amazement and shock, he could not believe what he was seeing. The young man rushed and stood in front of him, he started to stare at him like a person taking blood retribution would look at a murderer. The priest had become dumfounded.

The young man started mumbling in a low voice. "O person, do you know why has this girl died? She died because she had pledged her life to virgin mother Mary (Peace and blessings of God be upon her). Then after that, love had become a barrier in her way. She could not see any escape from her heart and from her religion, other than committing suicide. O the contractors of religion, these are your sins which you commit on the face of the earth. Was it not sufficient for you that already you had restricted marriages with your own hands? You make matrimony permissible for whom you chose, but then for others you make marriage inaccessible, like an unpayable loan. Without a doubt, that Supreme Being who has created us, the one who has moulded our spirits into our bodies; He is also the one who has created for us this heart and has created for us love. He orders us to love and live in this world with affection and prosperity. What right do you have to interfere between a person and his Lord, and between a person and his heart?"

He continued saying "Verily God is far and very high up in the skies. Our sight is constrained and it cannot reach there and neither can our senses meet with His senses. We do not have any method to see Him in His manifest beauty and magnificence, nor can we discuss Him through strange gesticulations other than observing His creation and loving them.

If you want us to live in this world without love, then take our throbbing hearts away from us. Only after that you can demand whatever you want from us. This is because we cannot stop loving until our hearts are beating."

Advancing further, he said, "O people! Do you think that we were created in this world only to be transferred from the darkness of the womb in to the blackness of a monastery, and then from the duskiness of the monastery into the darkness of the grave? If so, then how bad is our life and how immoral is our birth? This world contains no other virtue than the sanctification of love. We do not have any place of refuge where we can escape to from the sorrows and tribulations of life. So, before you sanction love itself, find and invent for us another place of refuge first."

Unrelenting, he said, "These birds which are singing in their nests, in reality they are humming the songs of love. This wind which is passing the atmosphere, this also is carrying the messages of love in its curves. These stars of the sky, these planets in orbit, flowers in their gardens, the greenery of the pastures and the bloom of the meadows, as well as animals and the insects of burrows, all of these, are living through the blessing of love. O hard hearted people, these dumb animals and the silent raw materials are more exalted than speaking human beings, and through the mercy of love they have more right to live than us. They are fortunate that whatever you say they do not understand and whatever you tell they cannot hear. This way, they are safe from misery, tribulations and everlasting misfortune."

Continuing his cry, he said, "O people, we do not know you neither do we recognise your religion. We do not want to overpower our bodies and our souls with your visions. We do not want to look at your faces neither would we like to listen to your voices. Therefore, hide yourselves from us and enter into your places of worship and caves because neither can we follow you nor can we live with you. Behind us there are delicate hearted women and weak minded men, we fear that your wickedness might reach them also. It is imperative that we become a barrier in your way, so that we can separate you from them, and that you cannot reach them in terms of brainwashing their lingering hearts and minds."

He added "We do not worship anyone other than God, He is one and we do not associate any partners with Him. It is through our own capability that we find our path towards Him, alone, without the guidance of people like you, so we do not require your help. Our book and signs of God, as well as the sweet says of nature, are sufficient for our belief. We do not require your articles of faith. The beauty of the heavens and the earth, the splendour of those who speak and those who are silent, and the loveliness of the stationary and the moving, all these are a crystal clear mirror in which we see the supreme majesty of God being illuminated. In front of God we fall in prostration, and then with full consciousness we motivate ourselves to Him so that we can listen to His command. God says, 'O people! I have created splendour and beauty only for you to enjoy, so enjoy it, and you were created to give life to beauty, so give life to it.' This is the command of God which we hear and obey beyond everything else."

At this point in his speech, his tongue became heavy, his courage gave up on him and his joints started to tremble. He fell down in his station and started taking severe warm sighs, complaining and lamenting. The old priest drew near him and, putting his hand on his forehead, said, "Son, have some patience and assurance, you are not the first on the face of this earth who is wounded with pain and sorrows, and neither was your beloved friend the first to depart from this world. The one who endures patience upon the blessing and the will of God, for him is reassurance, and for the pious there is a reward."

The young man took hold of his hands and kissed them. He said "O Father, forgive me my sin, I am from amongst the unjust."

The priest said "May God forgive you O son, verily the door of mercy is not closed, neither is there a barrier nor anything preventing it from closing."

The young man said to the priest, "O father, this girl was all alone on the face of this earth. Besides me she had no one. She died because of me and for me. Do you permit me to go near her and give her a farewell kiss in these last moments?"

The priest said "You do this O son." Hence, he rose upon his knees and crawled to her, upon reaching her he gave her a very tight hug. Then, placing his face upon her face, for the first time ever in his life, he gave her a kiss. With it, his soul had also departed.

***

These two martyrs were buried at the same time under the green, luscious tree which was next to the flowing river. Meanwhile, faraway an old neighbour went to visit the young man's mother, next to the open grave she used to sit and cry next to. This time, the mother was not present. She drew nearer to the ditch, only to find her enveloped in her sheet of cloth, stained with soil, without sense or motion; lying dead. Sighing, she filled up that five hand span gap of the grave with soil. That gap was the distinction between life and death. Then she shed one tear upon her grave, the overall lot which the dying lady had gained from this world.

THE VEIL

A man went to Europe, who had no bad habits. He stayed there for a few years and then returned. We could not recognize his good characteristics anymore, those which we used to see in him, they had perished.

He went with a face of humility, as if he was a lady on the first night of her wedding, and when he returned, his face was like the soft particles on soil of a rainy night. When he went, he went with a clean heart which was inclined towards forgiveness and compassion. However, when he returned, he had a hollow heart which was bitter against the land and its residents, full of mistrustfulness and jealousy. He was displeased and aggrieved with the heavens and their creator. When he went, he went with a freshly blooming heart, a soul full of humility, he saw everyone above himself. Nevertheless, when he returned, he returned with a sour personality and did not see anyone above himself.

He did not look at anyone with humility anymore. He went with a head which was full of wisdom and shrewdness. However, when he came back, his head resembled the sculpture of a punctured skulled, which was not full of anything other than deteriorated conjectures. He departed as if he did not consider anything on earth more beloved to him than his religion and his patriotism for his country. Though, when he had come back those things felt the most inferior to him on the planet.

I used to see the strange faces which weak young men used to bring back to their countries from these nations. Verily those colours of the West which colour their bodies, only last until the sun of the East declines. The Western colour extinguishes and its particles are flown away in the sky's atmosphere. For them, they consider foreign countries like a mirror for their faces. Whenever the face is turned from it, the reflection finishes within. I did not like to leave this friend alone. I had covered his faults for the sake of previous loyalty. I had tolerated him and hoped for him to leave his foolishness, his superstitions, his void perceptions and his strange ways. A person like me cannot endure this kind of behaviour, but I did, until he came to me at the beginning of one night in a stressful state with a severe problem.

In our meeting, I noticed that he was quiet and distressed. I offered my greetings to him and he replied with a gesture. I then asked him "What is the matter?"

He replied "Since last night, I have been upset with this woman over a matter which I cannot obtain redemption from. The decision which I have made in this matter, I see no fate in it."

I asked "Which woman are you talking about?"

He said "It is that woman whom the people address as my wife and I consider her to be a very big obstruction in the way of my desires and motives."

I said "Verily you have numerous desires O friend, which desire are you talking about?"

He said "I have only one desire in my life, which is that, I close my eyes and then open them to see that no woman in this town ever wears a veil covering her face."

I said "This, you do not have neither power nor opinion over."

He said "A lot of people share a similar view and desire to mine concerning the veil. There is only one barrier to them unveiling, revealing themselves and freely mixing with consenting men. This is the humility, weakness and fear which has always existed, typical of people of the East. Whenever courageous people attempt making a move for this modern change, they are stopped by old traditions. I see myself hastening to destroy these old customary foundations which are standing in between notional success and fortunes for a very long time. I see myself as a revolutionary, propagating the liberation and freedom of women, a task yet unfulfilled.

Thus, I presented this scenario to my wife, she esteemed it and considered it a valuable task. However, at the same time she acknowledged that I will be the one bringing upon her big trials, catastrophes and troubles.

She said 'If I reveal myself and start mixing in with the men, then I will not be able to socialize with the women after this anymore on the basis of shame and modesty.'

I say, in fact, here there is no humility and shame, but only immobility, death and a disgrace which God strikes upon the women of this country, who are forced to live in the darkness's of their graves within their veils and scarves. In death, they are then only transported from their worldly grave to that of the hereafter. Thus, it is crucial for me to materialise and complete my task, my desire. I will cure this head strong stubbornness or else break it in two."

From his conversation, my heart filled with sadness and sorrow. I looked at him, with eyes full of mercy. I said to him "O friend, do you know what you are talking about?"

He replied "Yes, I am speaking the truth in which I have firm belief, this is my perception, which is apparent in yourself and in the hearts of many people as well."

I said "Do you grant me permission, so I can say something to you? You have spent a long time living between a nation where there is no veil between men and women. Can your heart recall any day where you had wished for a woman whom you had no right over, and you were successful in obtaining her and yet her guardian was unaware?"

He said "That happened many times, but what are you getting at?"

I said "What I would like to say is that, I fear that people do not also tarnish your reputation the way you have blemished theirs, through the actions which you have committed."

He said "Certainly a modest woman has the power to live amongst men, and yet still safeguard her modesty and her chastity in a well-fortified fortress, so no seducer can present his desires."

Thus, he interposed me and I could not bear him, I said, "O you weak people, this is Satan's deception, penetrating through the corners of your heads, dismantling your brains and senses. Regarding modesty, this is not but a word, which has no room in linguistics and in dictionaries. Hence, if we try to investigate it from the hearts and through the sentiments of people, it is very rare that we will find it. The heart of mankind is like a stationary reservoir which is always extremely clean, however when a stone falls into it, it becomes tumultuous. Chastity is also a colour from the colours of the soul whose true essence is an essence within itself. It is very rare that these colours could endure the beams of a static sun."

He said "Do you deny the existence of modesty between people?"

I replied "I do not deny it, because I know that it does superficially exist, but only between the foolish and the weak. However, I do deny its existence, between the shrewd, capable men and the modern, skilful women who sit in seclusion with one another without a veil."

I further added "Which environment from this town would you like to expose your women and men in? Once, when an educated man was asked, 'Why have you not married?' His reply was that 'All the women of this town are my wives.' Amongst students, there are those who, for the sake of their modesty, hide their faces from the eyes of their friends. However, everyday, in their school bags are carrying pictures and letters from their lovers and admirers.

Amongst the rough and common people, a lot of them enter a house as despised servants, but leave as honoured son in-laws without marriage.

Thus after all of this, why are you still so stubborn about the subject of women? Why are you so passionate about discussing them, and veiling or their unveiling? What is so alarming about women obtaining freedom or being a captive? Have you fulfilled all the rights and the obligations of the nation which were demanded by you, that now you have decided to deluge others with these blessings?

Before you can teach any manners and etiquettes to the women, you must first turn the men into fine, noble gentlemen. Hence, if you are unable to do so, then without question you are unable to do anything for the women.

In front of you they are many doors of worthy causes, you can knock on any. However, leave this door closed.

Verily if you were to open this door, you will bring upon yourself great devastation and everlasting catastrophe.

Show me one man from amongst you, who has the power to withstand his desires when he is in front of a woman he admires? Then I will believe that a woman can control herself in front of a man whom she admires.

You want to create hardships for women, those which you do not even have the power to carry out. You are demanding from them that which you do not even find and recognise in yourself. Thus, you are endangering them in the combat field of a menacing life. You do not know whether women will benefit or be at a mere loss. I think that you are amongst the losers.

A woman has never come up to you with a complaint of injustice, neither has she demanded you to open her shackles and to release her from her captivity, so why do you then interfere between her and her affairs? Why do you discuss their issues so passionately, day and night?

Certainly they do not complain about your curiosities and your absurd behaviour, the annoyance which you create for them when you stand in front of them wherever they go and wherever they stand. You make the atmosphere very uncomfortable for them. Hence, they see no option but to confine themselves in their houses, regardless of the wishes of their household. They close the doors and close the curtains. They have become fed up of you and want to escape your prying. It is amazing that with your own hands you have imprisoned them. Then, you go and stand upon the door of their prison and cry and sympathise over their misfortunes?

You do not have any mercy for them, but you have mercy for yourself. You do not cry for them, but you cry over those gratifying days which you spent in your town, where there was unveiled beauty on display and the environment was full of immodesty and the drift of shamelessness. If it was up to you, you would cut off your nose in order to win back that immoral life which you have left behind. Verily in that life of yours, purity was contained in a water skin, veiled and closed. You continued puncturing its corners every day and purity, drop by drop, kept on dripping until the water skin became dry and shrivelled up. This was still not sufficient for you, as today you have come in order to open its knot only to discover that there is not even one drop of purity remaining in the water skin.

For a long time, The Egyptian women lived with peace and satisfaction in their houses. They were content with themselves and with their lives. They considered it a complete blessing, either in fulfilling their obligations, or to stand in front of their Lord, or to look at their children with affection, or to have a conversation with the neighbouring lady about herself and sharing her feelings and her secrets with her.

A woman saw the best piety out of all pieties to show humility to her father and to obey her husband and to keep him happy, this was considered a complete act of modesty. She understood the meaning of love and was unaware of the meaning of amatory and lustful love. Thus, she loved her husband because he was her husband the way she loved her child because it was her child. Other women considered love being the foundation of wedlock, but she thought that wedlock was the foundation of love.

Then, you came along, and said to them 'Those people of your house who overpower you with commands, they are not more intellectual than you, neither their opinion is superior to yours. They cannot watch out your welfare better than you. Therefore, they have no right and neither any authority to govern you the way they think they can.'

Due to your words, the woman now considers her father to be dishonourable, and has started rebelling against her husband. As a result, the house which yesterday was blooming with happiness and laughter like that of a wedding night, has become a dwelling of death, whose flames never extinguished or perished.

You said to her, 'It is inevitable for you that you select your husband yourself, so that your family cannot deceive and neither deprive you from your future fortune.' Hence, she made a bad selection for herself, which her family did not choose for her. Such a marriage prospers only for one day and one night, then it is followed by long hardships, and humiliating punishment after.

Then you said to her 'Certainly the basis of a marriage is love.' Thus, she started rolling, elevating and directing her eyes upon the faces of men until love affiliated with wedlock. Thus, this is how she took care of this matter.

Then you said to her 'Verily the prosperity in the life of a woman is that her husband must be her previous boyfriend and her lover.' Before this, she did not know anything other than a husband's love. Due to this, she went out in search for a new husband every day in order to revive the grieving love which had died with the old husband. Hence like this, she lost her old husband and could not benefit from a new one.

You said to her, 'It is vital for you to learn, so that you can educate your children beautifully and at the same time manage the system of the house.' Hence, she learnt everything, but failed in the upbringing of her children and the management of the household.

You said to her 'We only get married to the women who we love and the ones we are pleased with, making sure that our taste corresponds with theirs and that our feelings match their emotions.' Thus, she saw that certainly for her it was necessary to recognise the station of your desires and to work out what glitters in your eyes, so that she could adorn herself according to what you love. Hence, she examined the index of your life, page by page. She did not see in it anything other than the names of vulgar, shameless women, for pleasure and entertainment.

The men praised their intelligence and their mesmerising looks.

From this, she became unashamed and obscene as well in order to obtain your satisfaction and desire. Then she walked towards you, wearing very fine, thin transparent clothing, presenting herself to you the way a concubine would present herself in the market of slaves. When you saw this behaviour, you disliked and refrained from her. Saying, 'We men do not marry roguish and immoral women who have a bad character.' You did not care whether the entire nation of women becomes indecent, as long as your wives remain pure and sound. Thus, she returned with a broken and despaired heart, as now lecherous people do not like them and decent people refrain from them. Hence, she found in front of her a tumbling door, and fell in it.

In this way, doubt circulated in the hearts of the entire nation, and men and women started to have ill assumptions about each other. Both became desolate from each other and the atmosphere darkened between them. Their houses became like monasteries and a spectator could not see but men as priests and women as nuns.

O people of mercy! This is the reality of your cries, your mourning and your sympathising for the women!

Like you, we know that indeed women need education. Hence their fathers or brothers must teach them etiquettes because manners are more beneficial to them than knowledge. If she requires an honest and merciful husband, then her father should seek for his daughters a good husband. If the husband requires a good wife, then he should take good care of her and to take her out towards clean and fresh air in order to rejuvenate her and to enjoy the blessing of life. Thus, her guardians should give her the permission for this, along with allowing her companion to accompany her for her recreation activities at mornings and at evenings, the way a shepherd escorts his sheep due to the fear of wolves. If, however, we are unable to take a father, a brother or a husband to do this, then we should wash our hands away from the entire nation of men and women. This is because a woman does not have the capability of self-controlling her righteousness the way a man has the competence to reform her.

It is amazing that you have learned everything apart from this thing, which was near your understanding. This is vital for you to learn before everything. Certainly for every green land there is a specific grass which it cultivates, and that grass grows at exclusive times, this is when its progress and the green land becomes lush.

You have seen the scholars in Europe who indulge in the study/progress of sciences between their nations. Verily they are self-indulgent from all their needs. You have also become indulgent like them, enforcing their ideals on a nation whose majority do not even know the letters of the alphabet.

You have seen the philosophers there. Through their ill-founded intellect and etiquettes, they are propagating the philosophy of rejecting God between the branches of disbelief. This could deprive some from their faith. You have also started propagating the same element to a nation who are weak and simple, but unfortunately you cannot deprive them from their faith, even if there was something there to withdraw them from their belief.

You have seen a European man who is absolutely free, he does what he pleases, and lives the way he wants. This is because he has the power to look after himself and to watch his footsteps at a time when he knows that he has reached the boundary of freedom which he has specifically chosen for himself. He is careful not to transgress it. However, you intend to bestow this liberty to the one who is weak in his intentions and has scrawny objectives? A non-westerner is living his life with good conduct at the peak of a slanting, slippery rock. If his feet slip once, he will tumble in such a way that he will not have the ability to stop until he will fall into a ditch, and would deteriorate in its penetration.

You have seen a European husband whose dignity has been extinguished by the environment. The humility and modesty of his heart have been perished. He has the capacity to see another man put his hand around his wife's waist, whoever she is happy with. He is happy with her befriending whomever she wills and chooses to be alone with. Her husband will remain stationary, motionless and unaffected. Would you like that a high esteemed, simple Eastern man also stand back and withhold his honour the way this European man does?

Furthermore, have you seen a European wife? She is full of audacity and bravery. She can stand up in all situations with the men, and safeguard herself and her esteem. Do you think that such safeguarding is appropriate amongst the simple, naive and weak women of Egypt?

Every type of vegetation which is cultivated in a land other than its land or that it is planted in a time other than its time, is either rejected by the land or destroyed by it.

We are requesting you, for the sake of the country's honour and secrecy of religion, that you leave the remaining women alone who are living in their houses peacefully. Do not torment them with your dreams and wishes the way you have tormented women previously. For every wound there is an ointment other than wounded modesty. If you cannot refrain from doing this, then just wait a while, you will see that time will eventually strip away from your hearts that modesty and that integrity which you have inherited from your forefathers, and then you will live your new lives in baseless prosperity and in peace."

***

After I had explained everything, a sarcastic and hallucinating smile appeared on his young face. He started saying, "We have not come here but only to cure our foolish actions, hence we will be patient upon this until God decrees a verdict between us and them."

Thus, I said to him "You have the authority upon yourself and your household, thus do with them as you please. Permit me to say this, that after today I will not have the power to come and go to your house anymore, preserving you and myself, because I know the moment you will have the veil removed from your house and from the face of your wife, I will die out of shame and humiliation." Then I departed, creating separation between me and him.

Not even a few days passing by, I heard from people that, he had removed the veil between the men and women in his house. His house is always crowded with friends and upon his door there is always the noise of pounding shoes. Thus, my eyes shed a tear, I did not know that whether this was a tear of destroyed integrity, or a tear of grief for a lost friend?

This incident occurred three years ago, I did not go to meet him in his house and neither did he come to see me. I did meet him at times when crossing paths, I offered him greetings like how a stranger would to a stranger and then I carried on. During this time nothing was discussed, as then I left walking on that path altogether.

Yesterday I was returning home, the first part of the night had elapsed. Unexpectedly, I saw him coming out from his house and he appeared confused and perplexed. With him was a constable who was from the police department. It seemed like the police constable was supervising him, or that he was driving him out. Thus, I grieved and felt sorry for him in his dilemma. I drew near him and enquired about his affair.

Hence, he replied "I do not know anything other than that this constable has come now and knocked on my door to take me to the police station. I cannot find or work out the reason for this demand. I am neither a culprit nor am I a suspect. O dear friend, would it be possible for me to hope that you will spend this night in my company, despite that there is a friction between me and you, it might be that I may require some help from you if any matter was to arise?"

I said, "I will love to come with you." I walked with him silently, I did not talk to him and neither did he say anything to me. Despite our silence, I felt that he held something in his heart which he wanted to share with me, but shame and shyness hindered him.

Opening up the conversation, I asked, "Are you able to tell me what the reason for this call is?"

He looked at me with amazement and said "I fear that some event has happened with my wife tonight. I am in doubt about her because she has not returned home yet and this has never happened with her before."

I said "Was there anyone with her?"

He replied "No."

"Do you know where she had gone?"

"No."

"Over which thing are you fearful?"

He said "I do not fear of anything other than that I know she is a passionate and foolish woman, perhaps some people tried messing around with her on the way, then she must have quarrelled with them aggressively, and thus some incident must have occurred, because of which, the matter has reached the police station."

By now we had arrived at the police station. The police constable took us to the commanding police officer, and we stood before him. He gestured to the constable in front of us, giving a signal, which we did not understand. Then he requested the young man to come near, and said to him "Dear sir, I am sorry to inform you that indeed tonight the police men found a man and a woman from a suspicious location in improper circumstances and have brought them both to the police station. The woman has revealed her relationship to you, this is why you were called, so that you can disclose her matter to us. If she is truthful we will permit her to go with you, honouring and protecting your respect, and your humility will stay intact. Otherwise she is an adulteress woman who will have no escape and will be subject to being penalised for her crime. Both of them are now behind you, so look at them. The constable has brought them both from the other room."

My estranged friend looked and discovered that it was his wife, and the man with her, was one of his friends. Hence, he screamed so loudly that the walls of police station shook, the doors and windows turned into eyes and ears. Then he fell down in his place unconscious. I requested the police inspector to send the woman to her father's house. He did this, and let her friend go.

Then we took the young man in the car to his house and called a doctor for him. He was diagnosed with having a very severe brain fever. The doctor stayed awake next to him for the remaining night, treating him until morning drew near. He departed, saying that he will return whenever called, and made me responsible for his care. I sat next to my friend, feeling sorry for his condition. I awaited the decree of God in his matter, until I saw that he was making a movement in his bed.

He opened his eyes and saw me. He stared at me for a while, as if he wanted to say something but did not have the power to do so. Thus I drew near to him and said, "Do you require anything, dear?"

He replied with a low, weak voice "My requirement is that no one from the people should come in to see me."

I said "No one shall come in to see you other than who you want."

For a short while he looked down, and then he raised his head, as his eyes were saturated with tears.

I asked "Why are you crying dear?"

He asked "Do you know where my wife is now?"

"What do you want from her?"

"Nothing other than to say to her that verily I have forgiven her."

"She is in her father's house."

He said "May God shower his mercy upon her, her father and upon her clan. Certainly before they had established a relationship with me, they were highly noble and glorified. However, ever since they tied a connection with me I did nothing other than dress them up in a garment of nudity, which the time and destiny will not be able to eliminate.

Who is there for me to take this message to all of them? I am a patient who is near death. I fear that when I meet God, I will meet Him with their blood. Therefore, I am begging them to pardon me and to forgive me for my going astray before death overtakes me.

Indeed, I made a pledge with her father the day she was given to me that I will safeguard her respect the way I protect my life, that I will keep her protected from everything which I protect myself from. I was unable to keep my promise. So will he forgive me my sin so that God would forgive me through his pardoning?

Yes, indeed she is the one who has killed me. However, I was the one who placed that knife in her hand which she has pierced in my chest. Hence, no one should question her for my sin.

The house was my house, the wife was my wife and the friend was my friend. I was the one who opened the door of my house for my friend to reach to my wife. There is no one else to blame other than myself."

Then, after a short while, he stopped talking. I looked at him and saw a black cloud hovering upon his forehead, which gradually covered his face. He took such a warm sigh that I presumed that the curtain of his heart had burned. Then he said,

"Woe, how severe is the darkness in front of my eyes and how narrow is this world upon me. In this room, upon the sofa, under this roof, I used to see them two siting and talking to one another. My heart used to fill with joy and happiness, praising God that he has bestowed me a friend who socialises with my wife in her loneliness, and a kind, generous wife who respects my friend when I am not there. Thus, announce to all mankind, that verily this man, who yesterday used to boast about his cleverness and his wisdom, and labelled himself superior than all in intelligence and shrewdness, today declares in his dying breaths that he is the highest of fools, and that there is no degree of imprudence beyond his. Woe upon me, my mother should have never given birth to me, and my father should have had no sons in his destiny.

Perhaps people knew about my wife's affair. Perhaps, when I passed them, they looked at each other, winked at each other and smiled at one another. Maybe they would stare for a long time at my face in order to see how stupidity looks on the faces of the foolish, and how idiocy prevails on the faces of the idiots.

Perhaps those people, who loved me and made me their friend, only did so because of my wife and not because of me. Maybe those people addressed me as a pimp amongst themselves and considered my wife as a prostitute and my house as a brothel. I used to consider myself as the noblest from the people, and most respected.

May the Lord have mercy on me if I were to stay alive on this earth for another moment after today. Woe be upon the nook of the solitary in the fearful grave which will envelope me and envelope my nakedness with me."

Then he closed his eyes and returned to his slumber and unconscious state. During that moment, a midwife entered, and brought in his child, she placed him next to his bed. She left the child there and departed. The infant crawling besides him climbed up on the chest of his father, he felt him as he opened his eyes to see. He smiled at the toddler and cuddled him upon his chest with love and affection. He drew his face closer to his in order to kiss him.

After that he had a shivering fit, upsetting his happiness. He pushed the infant away severely with his hands, and screamed. "Take him away from me! I do not know him! I do not have a child nor do I have a wife! Ask his mother who is his father and take him to him! I will not bear shame in my life, and I leave him upon this slander forever after my death."

The midwife returned quickly after hearing the screech of the child, she picked him up and took him away with herself. The man heard the child's voice was slowly departing from him. He shouted so she could hear, "Bring him back to me."

The midwife brought him back and he took the child from her hands, observing his face closely, saying, "O son, for the sake of God, please forgive the inheritance of an orphan given to you from your father and the heritage of disrobe from your mother, pardon us both. Indeed, your mother was a weak woman, she was unable to control her instincts, so she fell. Your father's crime was only to do good and righteousness, however he sinned.

It is the same to me, whether you are my son or the son of your culprit mother through sin. Without doubt, this short time, I am very fortunate and lucky to have you, I will never forget the favour of happiness and the joy which you have given me whether I stay alive or die." Then, he took him in his lap and gave him a kiss on his forehead. I did not know whether this was a kiss from a kind father or a kiss from a generous caring being.

His state got better, but then his fever returned and his head started burning severely. Slowly and gradually his state became heavier. I feared that his time had drawn near so I sent someone to call the doctor. Hence, the doctor came and cast a long eye upon him. Then, in despair, the doctor removed the disheartened and sorrowful sight away from him.

The young man took his last breath and started sighing aloud, which was fearful. Every eye which saw became tearful, crying for his recovery.

We were sat beside him and indeed the dark curtains of death were gradually casting over his bed. At once, a woman who was enveloped in a black coverlet entered the room and approached him slowly. She inclined over him, and kissed his hand which was placed over his chest.

Softly, she spoke, "Do not leave this world with doubts about your son. Undeniably his mother acknowledges her fault in front you. You are departing towards your Lord, and I was near committing the sin of fornication but I did not commit it. Please forgive me O the father of my son. I will beg God that when you stand in front of Him, He joins me with you. This is because there is no good for me in my life after you."

Then she burst out in tears. Hence the man opened his eyes and looked at her with a smile. This was the man's last look in his life before he died.

***

Now, I have returned from the graveyard after I have buried my friend with my hands. I have entrusted this flourishing, radiant and glowing flower in the ditch of the grave. I have sat down now in order to write these lines and cannot gain control over my tears. My sighs, my sorrows and my feelings towards him are still not lessening. However, over this I am content, that indeed this nation was standing in front of a door of extreme danger. This man advanced and jumped into this danger alone. He stormed into it, and died the death of a martyr. Hence, his sorrowful example served as a clear warning to all, and he saved the nation from destruction.

THE REMEMBRANCE

The last king of Granada, Abu Abdullah, was standing upon the shore of the black sea under Mount Gibraltar in Spain, after losing to the army of King Ferdinand's and Queen Izabal's. He was waiting to embark on a ship which would transport him to Africa. In his surroundings, women, children and the nobles of the tribe of Banu Ahmar were standing. He gazed longingly upon the kingdom which he had lost and would not return, his eyes filled with tears. He drew his blanket near his face and cried excessively. He was making a very emotional heart touching sound, and the people who were standing beside him also started to cry. The sea shore became a place of death, which echoed sighs and cries. He was standing at a place where he had forgotten himself and his status. At once he heard a voice calling from the skies above.

He raised his head to discover that it was an old man reclining on a walking stick, standing at the entrance of a mountain cave. The old man began "Certainly O fallen down governor, you should cry upon your kingdom like women, because you could not safeguard your kingdom like men. Verily you were laughing yesterday, so now cry in the same proportion to your laughter. Verily happiness is the day of life and sorrow is its night. After a bright day the darkness of the night is inevitable.

Only if that kingdom that you had lost through your hands had been lost through the troubles of destiny or through a divine decree from the skies, which you had no strategy to overcome, nor command or control over. Verily you have disposed the kingdom with your own hands. You have handed over the kingdom to your enemy with your free will. Hence, cry over this like how a remorseful, shameful being would cry who cannot find any solace or comfort from his misery.

God does not allow injustice on any one from amongst his people, nor does He intend any evil or calamity to afflict them. However, it is the people who refuse, they stand on the corner of a deep ditch and take a deep breath and then their feet slip. It is the people who walk under visible rocks which then collapse upon their heads.

You were not content with the division of God which he had ordained for you from his provisions. You rejected it as you were only interested in the country and the kingdom. Hence, you quarrelled with your paternal uncle, then you sought help against him from your mutual enemy. Thus your enemy kept on pounding your heads together, making you fight with one another until a well of blood flowed under both of your feet, and both of you drowned within.

O Banu Ahmar, I have been waiting upon this mountain for seven years now, just to see the outcome of your foolish journey. I have been waiting for this moment to see such a leader leave, with no hope of return. This is because I know that when a guardian of a kingdom is a

72

fool and illiterate, then there is inevitably no progress or place for him in his land.

You have made enmity amongst yourselves, and every one of you has become an enemy for his companion. Thus, you have dragged out the Muslims towards the battlefields, they are killing each other while your enemy is kneeling down behind you and observing this, awaiting your loss in delight. The enemy saw every one of you as a commanding general who is waging a war with their enemy, attempting to exile them from his country. He saw you falling down due to weakness and fatigue, then he plunged into you, he patrolled around you one or two circuits until he obtained victory from you.

Soon you shall stand in front of God, O the leaders of Islam. Soon you shall be asked about the Islam which you had lost and whose elevated dignity and status you brought down to the dust. You are going to be asked about the Muslims, whom you have entrusted to your enemy with your own hands, so that they can live amongst them in a life of degradation and weakness. God will ask you about the Islamic civilisations and the cities which your forefathers had bought with their blood and their lives, then they had left them for you so that you can safeguard them and honour them. Thus you stayed constant and still until your enemy overpowered you. Hence you started living a despised life, and they drove you out like strangers and trespassers. So, what would be your answer if tomorrow you are asked about all of these things?

Look! The church bells are ringing here upon the minarets instead of the Azan (call to Muslim prayer). Take a look, the cross bearers' shoes are trampling over the Mosques on the ground where the foreheads of the Muslims used to touch. What kind of Muslims are these who are running from one place to the other with their religion, taking refuge upon the peaks and gates of mountains? They do not have the power to fulfil any religious obligations whatsoever, but they are in a cave similar to the one I am in.

Only if the Muslims lived their lives in their eras without a government, without a country and without a king, the way the homeless live in the corners of the cities. Verily, this was a better option for them than being ruled by men who are like themselves, greedy and unjust. They have put a big shackle on their necks and are dragging themselves towards the place of destruction and loss, defenceless and unable to retaliate against the totalitarianism.

God will question you, 'O Banu Ahmar! About me and about my children, those who you snatched away from my hands, even though I needed them a great deal. You dragged them towards the battlefields so that they could fight their Muslim brothers. Here, there was no nobleness and honour, yet they all died the death of inferiority and lowliness. Why did you not leave them besides me so that I could have had their company in my loneliness, and I would have requested their help in my senile old age?

Why did you not take them towards the battlefield in honour, so that I could have found solace in knowing that they had died as martyrs for their religion or for their country as patriots?

Take a look, I am living all alone after them in this fearful cave on top of this segregated rock, crying over them and asking God to join me with them. Oh, when is God going to respond to my supplication?"

Then, because of crying, his throat became asphyxiated. He turned his face away and walked off with the aid of his stick to his cave, disappearing from sight.

The ruler was astonished with his words, even he was not as sorrowful as this man about losing his kingdom and the collapsing of his throne. Hence, he screamed and said, "This is not a man, verily this is the voice of justice which is scaring me about the future misfortune, which is more severe than the calamities of the past. God can do what He pleases with me, because justice is with Him and He can do whatever He wills."

Then he progressed towards his ship, and his family followed behind him. Cutting through the waves of the water, the ship set off, carrying them inside it. History had written down this event in its pages, and this was the time that indeed the exile of the Arabs from Andalus Spain, had been complete. The Arabs prior to this had ruled Spain for eight hundred years.

***

Twenty-four years after the incident, not even one soul remained alive from Banu Ahmar, other than a young man who was twenty years of age. His name was Saeed. He did not see Granada nor did he see the Qasr al-Hamra. Neither did he see the meadows of Granada nor the Generalife (Jannatu-l-'Arif). He did not see the Ebro river, the Sierra Navada nor the mountain of snow. However, he always had its vision seared in his memory, memorised through the songs of Andalus which the ladies of his nation used to sing in his childhood, besides his cradle. In those songs there was mention of his father, his grandfather, of their works, and the honour of their Kingdom which existed in their army. He also remembered the painful song, upon which the poets of Andalus had cried. That is, fallen dignity and wasted kingdom. Thus, whenever he was alone, he hummed the tune of these old folksongs, glorifying the traditions of his ancestors. He used to sing them with a lot of passion, a great depth of feeling, which inflamed his pain and tears. Sometimes, he used to cry and scream so much that he used to draw close to his death.

For himself, he never desired anything from God the way other people did, other than that he wanted to see Granada only once in his lifetime, so that he could be satisfied and consoled. After that, he wanted to leave his affairs to the discretion of destiny, which will choose for him whatever it wills.

Whenever he intended to go to Granada, he ended up sitting back down with the thought of leaving an old woman behind him, who was from his family. He did not have the power to leave her nor did he find anyone who he could trust to look after her if he was to go. Eventually, her time also came, and she met her Lord.

Hence, he embarked on a journey through the ocean from the Sabie River in Africa, all the way to the corner of Mula, Spain. Then, he advanced towards Granada disguised in an Arab Doctors dress, appearing to be seeking herbals upon the mountains of Andalus. He finally reached outside the town at evening time. He ascended upon the peak of an icy mountain. Here, he saw the water which was descending very peacefully as if its sparkling and glittering surface had a luminous shirt over it, or that it was a dome made out of crystal. When this water reached the ravine, it appeared like white, frightened snakes that scattered everywhere, as if trying to save themselves, escaping through a brook and hiding themselves within.

Then he turned his attention towards the city. From far, he saw some burgundy towers. High, prestigious domes and tall minarets, which were talking to the sky. Thus, he became stationary in front of this astonishing sight, in full humility and respect. He put his hand over the other, and placing them above his chest, as if he is standing in front of a mihraab, offering his prayer and remained in that position for a while.

Then, he announced in a very loud voice which echoed all over the woodlands and the jungle.

"This is the inheritance of my father and my grandfather. There is nothing remaining for me from this heritage other than this separation. This separation is similar to the agony of a devastated mother when she parts from her son. These are their beds in which now their enemies sleep in. However, in reality, the bedding of the enemy was nothing other than the sand of the desert upon small rocks at night.

These are their castles which are looking at the open atmosphere of the land. Their windows are the eyes which are looking at them in such a way that they appear in wait hoping that they will return and dwell again. However, they will not do this.

These are their domes and minarets which raise their heads towards the sky day and night, supplicating to God imploring, 'Bring back their carers and guardians', but their beseeching is not accepted.

It is these gardens in which they used to rest. Under these shades they used to sleep. Upon these river banks they used to spend their days and nights. However, today, there is no one from amongst them who could do his morning here neither anyone to do the night. Under this sky there is no one who is coming or going."

Then he looked towards the horizon, he saw the sun setting from the West, he saw that the army of night was empowering the defeated army of day, and dispersing through the sky. He fell to the ground, head first, and starting saying,

"Like this the governments change and like this the crowns fall. It is like this that darkness prevails in places of light. It is like this that the clouds of death scatter over the faces of life."

Then he turned with the aid of his hand, and fell into deep sleep above the bed of the earth and under the roof of the sky. He did not wake up until the kingdom of night had passed. Thus, after awaking, he walked towards the flowing river which was under the mountain, and offered his morning prayer.

After that he departed towards the city in order to seek lodgings/ a hotel where he could take shelter. He did not find in his way anyone who could guide him towards where he wanted to go until he reached the Ebro river. Then he walked towards its corner and began searching for seeds and herbals. He remained there in wait for the residents of the city to wake up.

He was in this state when suddenly before him a large castle door opened. There, he saw a Spanish girl coming out from it. Her face was veiled with a transparent black veil and upon her chest there was a small golden cross hanging off. Behind her there was a boy walking, holding a holy book. Surprised to see him, she glanced at the place where he was standing. She drew closer to him and lifted her veil from her face. She was extremely beautiful, and stunning like the sun in full beam. In a language which comprised of Arabic and non-Arabic she said to him "O young man, are you a stranger in this town?"

He replied "Yes, verily I have come here just now, I do know the way to an inn where tourists can take sanctuary. Neither have I found anyone who could guide me towards it."

The girl sensed modesty and nobleness in his voice, and the signs of happiness and bliss appeared on her face. She became considerate towards him. She gestured towards him and told him to follow her for guidance and direction. They walked side by side until they reached a motel. She gave her regards to him with a smile and in a very honourable way she said to him "O stranger, do not forget your meeting with me, whenever you are in need of anything, just ask." Then she walked towards the church.

***

A human heart is always circulating in between different desires and emotions collectively and individually, until it reaches the age of puberty and the sun of love rises upon him dimming and overpowering in front of him all previous desires and emotions. It is like how the different stars circulate in the sky of a darkened night, lighting up the night's sky, and the bright flame circulates, glowing up its dark corners until the sun rises from the east, and dims the brightness of all previous lights.

Thus, indeed at many instances, the prince looked at Granada from a different perspective than before. In the face of Granada, he saw the face of love after the face of terror. He saw light after darkness and he saw life after death. Hence, he forgot his fear and felt a cool breeze in his heart. The sharpness of his previous anger cooled down, and was steaming between his ribs. Thus, when he passed by a mosque from amongst the mosques of Granada, which were converted to churches now, he stood there for a while so that he may see that Spanish girl from amongst those who entered and came out.

Whenever he saw a cross on top of a minaret he remembered that beautiful gold cross which he saw upon the chest of that Spanish girl on the day they had met. The hatred with which he previously viewed such objects had been replaced with love, as they now reminded him of her, not his past. Whenever he heard the church bells ringing surrounding the atmosphere, he remembered the time when he saw that Spanish girl. This was because he heard the church bells ringing at that time when he had met her. Hence, he became content every time he heard the church bells and his heart became relaxed.

Like this, every morning, that poor gentleman used to go to the river bank of River Ebro for an outing. There he rolled his eyes upon the doors of the big castles, hoping that he may recognise the castle of that Spanish girl, but unfortunately did not. He used to observe the faces of girls who had passed in the mornings and evenings, hoping that he might see her. However, he was unable to do so. When he became hopeless, he returned to the graves of his forefathers which were visible in the town. There, he sat in between them and shed his tears in abundance. He did not know whether these tears were of his devastating past, or the pining of his present love.

***

Two years before this time, great trials and calamities had descended upon Florinda. The pain drawn from this has still not parted from her heart even today. Verily her father was the chancellor and the president of this state, which, for a few years, was in heavy opposition against its administration. Their aim was to give its residents complete liberation to practice their religion and claim their self-identity, despite their religion and identity. They continued this struggle until they became completely exhausted from doing their duty.

A secret conspiracy was devised to assassinate the president under the veil of darkness, and he was executed. After this, his daughter Florinda was devastated. She was also deeply saddened over her mother's death. Her mother had died worrying severely about her husband, who had never parted from her, and stayed with her mornings and nights.

When Florinda became eighteen years of age, she retreated to her castle, living a monastic life. Any onlooker only saw her coming or going to the church with her servant, or standing upon the signs, marks and the customs of the old government. They saw her observing these from every angle and it appeared that she was taking heed of them. Some saw her in the beauty spots and recreation parks of Granada, walking in a melancholy and distressed manner until the darkness veiled the night with its curtains. Then, after that, she returned to her castle. This was the state which she had always remained in. The people of Granada used to address her as the beautiful nun.

One day Florinda was passing by the graves of Banu Ahmar, there at once she saw a young Arab man from a distance. He was facing down kneeling over a grave and it appeared that he was kissing the surface of the grave and was making the soil of the grave wet with his tears. She felt sorry for him and she walked towards him until she drew near. The young man heard her sound and raised his head. He recognised her and she recognised him.

She said "O young man, are you crying over your Kings which existed yesterday? Cry, cry as much as you want because the soil of their graves has become dry as there was no one to cry over them."

That young man said "O dear, are you also upset over them?"

She replied "Yes certainly, indeed they were great people. The period and time has trampled over them. Certainly these people have more right to be cried over than anyone else from amongst the great fallen people."

He said "Thank you very much O respectable lady, this is the first time I have felt the garment of consolation creeping over my heart, ever since I have laid my feet upon this land of yours."

She said "Have you seen their castles and their symbols which they have left behind in this country?"

The gentleman for a little while put his head down and then he raised his head as there was a drop of tear hovering in his eyes. He said "No O respectable lady, I did intend to go near them but the guards who were guarding the doors threw me out. They are unaware that, from all of the living people, I am the only one individual who has more right to see them."

The lady said "Are you connected to any one from amongst their companions, are you a descendant of theirs, or are you their child?"

He said "No O respectable lady, I am but their freed slave, I was born in their hands, through their mercy. They handcrafted, planted their love in me which I shall never forget till I am alive."

She said "If you meet me here in this place at the same time tomorrow, I will take you wherever you would like to go."

He replied "If you were to do this, then in this world there is never going to be anyone more thankful to you than me." Thus, she offered her greetings and departed. The young man also proceeded to his hotel with mixed emotions of love and hope, which was killing him, and at the same time giving him life.

Florinda fulfilled her promise to her Arab friend, and the next day she came. She showed him some places. Then on the third day she came and showed him more sights. Like this, they kept on meeting and parting every day. Wherever they wanted, they went to see the old landmarks. The people who used to see them never thought badly of them. Whenever they saw them together they presumed that the beautiful nun is intending to guide and incline the Arab gentleman towards her religion.

As time went on, the kindness that she felt in her heart for him turned into burning love. Like this, kindness always becomes the road towards love, or it is the love itself which becomes a garment for the non-clothed. Not even one of them revealed what feelings they had for each other in their hearts, until that day came when the gentleman intended to visit the Qasr al-Hamra, as this was the last historical sight which yet remained. After this, both of them never met again for sightseeing.

***

The prince stood in front of the Qasr al-Hamra. He saw that the sky was in battle with another sky. One big mountain was colliding with the Gemini sky. One highland was highest amongst all other highlands. The clouds were passing by above other clouds. The mountain was so high, to observe it, eyes became tired, and the intellect failed. There is a castle nearby, which the vicissitudes of time could not remove. The days and years have passed by besides it. He entered and saw a very big city which had gardens and silk in it. He saw huge domes, over which the stars dotted with joy. There were towers there, on whose surfaces destiny had spread its hands over. The floor of the courtyard was made of faint pebbles as if it was a bright garden. The walls were glossy and soft, and became mirrors for everything in front of them. They were clear like a mirror in which reflect the faces of beautiful women. Its walls were full of waves which contained delight in them, like a sheet of glass. He passed by the sights with respect, amazement and awe, humming poetry,

I stood close to the Qasr al-Hamra shedding tears
and taking heed from it,

I was Lamenting, I said "O Qasr al-Hamra is the
return possible?"

It replied "Do the dead ever return?"

I kept on weeping at its traces.

Woe upon woe, only if the tears could give some
benefit?

As if those who have left their trails behind,
them trails have become the crying women who are
crying over the dead.

After this, he reached the biggest courtyard. He saw that
the floor of the courtyard was made out of yellow marble,
there were tall, slim pillars, upright, and lining all four
corners. In the corners of the courtyards, there were
rooms with high domes on them. Thus, he understood that
these were the rooms of the princes and princesses from
amongst his family. Hence, past memories flared up in
his heart and he felt it was going to explode due to the pain
and agony that he was feeling. He was compelled towards
crying, but he withheld his tears in front of Florinda. He
left her busy observing some of the architecture, and went
towards some other rooms. First he laid his eyes upon one
line of writing, which was inscribed upon a door. When
he read it he yelled out "O father," and fell in a swoon.

After a long time, he gained consciousness. When he
opened his eyes he found his head placed in the lap of

Florinda and he discovered that she had tears in her eyes. She said "Indeed I knew from before this day that you were hiding something from me, a secret in your heart, and verily I am convinced now that you are neither the slave of Banu Ahmar nor are you their freed slave the way you said, but you are one of the princes'. Indeed, you are in the castle of your grandfather and you are in front of your father's room. O Banu Ahmar, it is amazing to what degree you have been aggrieved. O poor prince, how unfortunate are you?"

After this, the prince did not find any other way to hide his affair. Thus, he began narrating his family's story to her, and what they suffered at the hands of destiny since they were exiled from Andalus, up to the present day. However, when he had finished narrating his story, he gave her melancholy look and said,

"O Florinda, indeed all of them misfortunes which I had received yesterday, are unquestionably smaller than those misfortunes which I shall receive tomorrow."

She said "Which misfortune is it that you are waiting for, is it greater than that misfortune which you are already in?"

He became silent for a while, then he raised his head and said "Verily, I have the power to bear everything in life other than the fear of parting from you, and not ever meeting you again."

She said "O prince do you love me?"

He said "Yes, the way a thirsty dried up flower loves a drop of rainwater."

She said "Do you have the power to love me, a Christian girl who does not belong to your religion?"

He replied "Yes, certainly the path of religion to the heart is different from the path of love. Verily I have found in you those attributes which I love, thus, I love you for them. After this, I will not be dishonoured by anything you believe in."

She said "Do you have love without any expectation?"

He replied "Why not? Love itself is the verge of every happiness in life, if it is destined for us. When we reach the perimeter of love, we obtain the ultimate bliss of life." The night verily had become dark. Hence, both of them got up from their station and walked and talked until both reach the place where they parted. Florinda placed her hand in his hand and said "O prince, soon I shall also love you the way you love me and my love for you will be unconditional. If religion has created a distance between our bodies, love will join our hearts together." Then, she left him there and departed.

After this, they became happy together, and enjoyed days filled with contentment and pleasure, making them forget their previous calamities and catastrophes. Above the land of Granada and under its sky, both of them became two beautiful birds which flew wherever they wanted to in the open air. The worlds surface glittered up for them, and they flew, sang and pecked wherever they pleased.

If only the people had ignored them and left them both alone in their world. If only the society had given them respite for a little while, to let them enjoy the bliss of life for a few moments, which they had bought in exchange for an abundance of tears and masses of tribulations. Other than this happiness, neither of them were the possessors of any other happiness. Thus, if they lost this happiness they would lose everything.

One day during this difficult time, both of them were sitting by a stream. Dan Roderick, the son of the governor of Granada passed by them. He saw both of them sitting together and they did not see him. Dan Roderick had seen Florinda before and had adored her. For a few days he kept on coming and going to Florinda's house, declaring his love for her and proposing marriage. Florinda adamantly refused his proposal and said to him "I will never ever marry the son of my father's killer." Swallowing his anger, he had left, and ever since he had been hiding his rage in his heart, until this day. Now, as he saw her sitting down, he speculated in his heart that Florinda had closed the door of her heart for him only because she had opened her heart for the handsome Arab man who was sitting with her. The next day, he went to her castle in order to reveal what he had in his heart for her. Florinda refused to meet him. He left the castle raging and fuming. He had a very callus and cruel idea of revenge in his heart.

A few days passed by, the prince, Saeed bin Yusaf, the son of Abu Abdullah, was dragged in front of a court for investigation. This was very humiliating for this progeny of Banu Ahmar, whom yesterday were the kings and the protectors of this land and its welfare and dignity, the makers and the owners of its castles and gardens. The criminal slander pelted on him was that he was forcing a Christian woman to leave her religion. This was considered the biggest crime one can ever do against the state.

The prince stood in front of the magistrate in order for his case to be analysed. The judge questioned him about the allegation made about him. The gentleman denied this accusation. Nevertheless, the judge did not care about his refuting this contention and said to him "There is no other proof of your innocence other than you leaving your religion and accepting the religion of Christianity." The prince raged with anger, he yelled out aloud, and his voice echoed through the courtroom.

He said "In which book from your books, and which covenant from the covenants of your Prophets and Messengers, is written that the punishment of those who do not adopt a religion like yours, and do not accept your religion is death? From which world under the sky and above the land have you obtained this understanding, that people are forcefully dragged towards religion? Is this how beliefs are spread, like how alcohol and water is drunk?

The day you came to this town, you took an oath, where is that oath? In that oath you pledged that you will give us our democratic right to practice freely our religions and our beliefs. In that oath you vowed not to harm us, wherever our hearts inclined, and also not to harm us in our religious ceremonies.

All this that you are doing today, is this what you promised to do yesterday? This, what you are doing certainly qualifies as the fulfilment of the pact, and a means to safeguard its citizens!

Yes, certainly you people can do whatever you please as verily the town has been emptied for you and you are the people of power and the kingdom is yours. Is this the dignity and respect of the rulers that they cannot fulfil and honour their pledge?

Verily that pledge which is between the powerful and the weak, in reality it is like a powerful sword which amputates the hands of the former and it is a shackle which is chained around the necks of the latter. May God never pardon the mistakes of the foolish and may He never allow ease/coolness for the eyes of the unwise.

You are the people of power and we are the people of weakness. You are upon clear truth and proof, so you can initiate whatever you want. This is your right which you have obtained through the power which you have been granted. You may spill our blood the way you please and you may strip away our rights the way you want. You can captivate our minds and our intellects so that we do not accept any other religion other than yours, and that we do not go towards any other religion but wherever you intend us to go. Hence-away with you! We are discharged from being amongst the powerful. It is inevitable for us that we have a share from that what the weak people obtain and receive."

Then the Prince tried his best to continue with his words, but the Judge cut him off and ordered that he be taken to the same public square where ten thousand Muslims were massacred and burned before. Thus, he was dragged towards this place of execution. Men and women gathered around his place of slaughter. Before the executioner even raised his sword upon the head of the prince, within the midst of the crowd, people heard the scream of a woman. They quickly looked, but did not recognise where the voice had come from. It only took the twinkling of an eye and the princes' head fell on the ground in front of everyone in a manner that could not be compared to anything else.

***

Even today, when a passer-by walks besides the graveyard of Banu Ahmar in Granada, he sees a beautiful embellished grave which is constructed from a yellow, clean, transparent stone. Under its surface there is a shallow dent, which collects rain water. Thus, the birds take refuge towards this on scorching days in the summer, and drink water from it. On one side of the grave, these lines are inscribed,

This is the final grave of Banu Ahmar.

From his loyal friend who fulfilled his pledge until death.

(Florinda Philip)

THE ABYSS

To what proportion are the days of life plentiful and to what proportion are they less?

I have spent many years living in this world. However, in reality I have only lived for one year. That year which I had lived passed by me like an ancient star which passes in the sky at night only once, then no one sees it after that ever again.

I spent the first portion of my life in search of a sincere friend. I was looking for a friend who would not look at his friends with an eye of a merchant inspecting his stock. Neither did I want a friend who would observe his friends with an eye of a farmer, who inspects his cattle. I encountered many friendship failures until I met someone whom I had known for eighteen years. In him, I saw great qualities, and characteristics, a good person with good etiquettes, the friend which I had long been seeking.

I did not find these attributes in anyone else except him. Whenever I imagined the face of a man belonging to the most excellent character, his face would sparkle and glitter in my mind. Thus, I held him in high esteem and respect. He made a place in my heart the likes of which no one had ever made before, and our cup of friendship overflowed with brotherly love.

There was nothing which faded away our friendship until, due to some unseen circumstances, I was forced to leave my place of residence, Cairo, and move back to my home town. I was not grieved upon anything except the saddening of the separation of this generous friend. For some time, we wrote to each other. After, his letters started decreasing, eventually they completely stopped.

I became severely upset over this. I started having all kinds of assumptions and concerns about him, though I never doubted his friendship and loyalty. Whenever I intended to travel to him and see how he was doing, my personal circumstances did not allow me to do so.

Thus, I only returned to Cairo after a couple of years. The day I set my foot on the land of Cairo, I had intended first to go and see my friend. I went to his house in the first portion of the night. When I got there I witnessed an atmosphere which even today it is connected to my heart.

When I had left this house, it was like the spirit of a small garden from amongst the highest gardens of Paradise, where people could see all different colours of life shining, and observe the faces of its residents glittering with tranquillity and peace. Today, I have visited the same house only to discover that I am standing in front of a graveyard, frightening and scary, surrounded with silence. There was no voice which was echoing in the house nor in any corner could a human being or a kindling lamp be seen. I presumed that I had mistaken it for another house, or that I was in front of an abandoned house. I was pondering on this matter when I heard the cry of a small baby. I saw a very vivid light coming in through some of the windows of the house.

Consequently, I walked towards the door and knocked. No one answered so I knocked once more. Then I saw some light coming out through a crack of the door. It was not long after that I saw the face of a small boy, who was dressed in old rags. He was holding a lamp in his hand which was fairly bright. When I concentrated upon his face through the light of that lamp, I saw in him the face of his father. I had recognized that certainly he is that beautiful pampered boy whom yesterday was the flower of this house and the star of its sky. I asked him about his father. He gestured to me to come in and he walked in front of me holding his lamp, until he took me to a very unclean hall which was extremely dusty.

In that large room there were deteriorated sofas placed and very old curtains hanging down. Despite the darkness, I recognised some old inscriptions and wall markings which had remained, without them I would have never recognized that certainly this is that same room where we had spent our blissful and fruitful nights for twelve months. Then a brief conversation took place between me and the youth. He had recognized who I was and I also gathered that his father had not returned home as of yet, and that he would be shortly. Then, he left me and went away. He returned briefly to say that his mother would like to talk to me regarding his father. My heart started beating fast out of fear and fright. I felt certain that some calamity had befallen which I had no idea of.

I turned back to discover that there was a woman wrapped in a black blanket standing upon the door step. She greeted me, and I greeted her as well.

She asked me "Do you know that after you had gone what role destiny played with your friend?"

I replied "No" and explained that this was the first day I was returning to this town ever since I had parted seven years ago.

She said "If only you had stayed, you were his protection, you protected and shielded him from the evils and catastrophes of life. Ever since you left him, a group of people belonging to the party of Satan surrounded him. As you know, your friend was a straight forward person, a man of good conduct. The men of Satan kept on motivating and inclining him towards evil and would beautify for him evil the way the devil glorifies evil for people, until your friend landed right in it, and subsequently we all fell into that ditch of misfortune as well, as you can see."

I said "O my respectable lady, which evil are you talking about? And who are those surrounding people, causing his fall?"

She said "I will tell you everything, the whole story, listen to what I have to say. He was a man walking in good pathways until he joined connections with his superior manager and became linked with him. Your friend then became one of his closest associates, and never parted his company wherever he went. His associates followed him morning and evening. From that day, his state changed and his good conduct transformed also. He started becoming disconnected with his wife and children. He only used to see us a little from time to time, and would return home in the last portion of the night. Verily at the beginning, I was really happy that he had attained a promotion with his director and drawn closer to his heart. I hoped that good was to proceed this and so I pardoned him from his regular absences from home. Despite that, I would fear and was saddened over his disconnection with me and his refraining from the affairs of his wife and children. The matter continued until he returned home one night completely distressed, sighing and experiencing severe fatigue and bodily pain. I drew near him and smelled alcohol from his mouth. From then on, I understood everything.

I realised that certainly this high ranking official is the leader of his subordinates. If he were to walk the good path, he would be doing good with his juniors. If, however, he was to tread upon the evil path, then only bad would be obtained by his subservient workers. He took my poor young husband upon the bad path, and the worst way. He did not consider him as a friend the way my husband had assumed, but as a drinking partner. I requested, pleaded before him, for the sake of everything he loved, hoping these things would separate him from his wayward boss. I shed so many tears before him with all the power I had in my eyes. I was hoping that he would return to his former life where he had lived in prosperity with his wife and children. Alas, my tears were unsuccessful.

After a while it came to my attention that, that same hand which took him towards alcohol had also taken him towards gambling. This did not surprise me because I knew that certainly the path to evil is one. If one is standing on its starting point, it is inevitable for him to pass all the way through until he reaches its end.

Subsequently this noble and gallant young man whom yesterday used to refrain even from the medicine where he had smelled alcohol from, and was ashamed to sit down in the gathering of those who drank, became a drunkard, a gambler, a loafer and completely shameless himself. He did not care about his respect, neither was he bothered about any insult. He would not refrain from his shameful behaviour, nor would let go of his sins. My husband was once a kind father and merciful, noble husband, who never allowed even an ant bite to his children. Neither did he allow another man to look at his wife with lustful eyes. Now, he became a hard hearted father and a tyrant husband. Whenever his children would go to him he would start beating them up. If he looked at me, he would start swearing and abusing.

This once sentimental and devoted man, who used to safeguard his honour and his respect, simply did not care anymore and would come home some nights with some of his roguish and rascal friends. Thus, he used to bring them upon the upper floor of the house where me and my children were sleeping. Then they would sit in one of its rooms and would drink, gamble and make a lot of noise, until alcohol used to dominate their senses and they would lose control. Then they would start singing and dancing and would fill the atmosphere of the house with screams and cheering. Then they would run and chase each other in the passages of the house, entering different rooms until they would enter and take refuge in my room.

Most of the time, they would stare at my face, and try to pull my scarf off while my husband watched and heard, but he would not say anything or stop anything. Then I would run from one place to the other in front of them. Most of the time, I ran out of the house altogether without a coverlet neither a scarf. Only the coverlet and the scarf of the night would cover me at that point. Then I would go to the next door house of my neighbour and spend the remaining night there."

Here, her tone of voice changed and she withheld her conversation and put her head down. I realised that she was crying. Internally, I started crying as well. Then she raised her head, and, returning to her conversation said "Not even a few years have passed since, that your friend has spent all that wealth which he had possessed. Then it became necessary for him to take out a loan, which he did. The load of the loan increased and he started pawning things. When he was unable to pay back, he sold his possessions, even this house we are living in. Now, nothing remains in his hand other than a meaningless monthly salary. In fact, it does not even remain in his hands anymore. Very soon after receiving his salary, it quickly become the ownership of his debtors or a win for his gambling companions.

This is what the hands of destiny have done to him. Myself and his children are also in great hardship, one complete year has passed since I have sold my last piece of jewellery. Now all my jewellery, clothes and household furniture are in the pawning shops, and in the shops of the debtors. My house and all its contents are deposited with pawn brokers. I have a close considerate relative, who, despite being in strained circumstances himself, has helped me occasionally with a little money saved by holding back on his own children. Without him, me and my children would have certainly died out of hunger.

O sir, maybe you have the power to help my husband, and save him from his problems and adversities. You hold a very sentimental and good opinion about him. I think that indeed you have the power to do this, because the station and the respect which he has in his heart for you, all mankind are deprived of it. Thus, if you were to help him, then you would be doing him, and all of us, a very big favour. It will be a huge act of kindness upon us, which we will never forget until death."

Thereafter she said goodbye to me and departed on her way. Then I asked the boy what time I would be able to see his father at home. He said "You can see him in the morning before he goes to his office." I walked out in my shocked state. I was concealing a burning restlessness in my heart, and the slumber of sleep had disappeared from my eyes. The night passed by, but it did not pass by easily.

I returned in the morning of the second day in order to see my old friend, who yesterday I used to consider being the best from all people. I did not know what would be the outcome after our meeting. My heart became anxious and petrified, like the heart of one who enters a racecourse as a competitor, spending on it all his wealth with no knowledge whether he shortly will win or lose, become the most fortunate or the most wretched.

***

Now I have realised that certainly faces are the reflections of hearts. If the heart sparkles the face brightens up. If the heart becomes darkened, the face likewise becomes gloomy. I had parted from this man seven years ago, and, because of this long gap, I had forgotten his face. I only remembered in it a glowing bright light, the light of excellence and dignity, which shone like the glow of the sun upon his face. However, when I saw him now, I did not see that luminous white light which I had once known. I thought to myself that I was seeing a face which was not the face of the past, and the man who I am looking at is not the man who I knew from before.

I did not see in front of me that beautiful young man who was always in laughter and his face brightened with smiles. In his place, I saw a distressed and unfortunate man who wore the dress of old age before old age had struck him. It appeared that he had reached the age of sixty, despite not even being thirty. His eyebrows were droopy. His eyelids were heavy. His sight became motionless, and cheeks were dangling down. His forehead was fallen down between his shoulders like a hunchback. The first thing which I said to him was, "O my dearest friend, everything has changed about you, even your face has changed." It was like he knew what was in my heart, and had recognized that I knew everything about his affairs. Thus, he lowered his head like the one who acknowledges that the place under the earth is better than the earth above. He did not say anything. I drew nearer to him and I put my hand upon his shoulder and said,

"By God, I do not know what can I say to you. Can I offer you advice? In the past, it was you who used to give me advice, you were the star of my guidance from which I used to brighten up my darkened life. Or, can I alert you towards what God has ordained for you in respect of you and your wife? I do not recognize what you have become? I cannot advise you on the best way to withdraw from this life. Can I request you to be kind towards your weak children and be merciful towards your poor distressed wife? This is because none of them have any support save you, neither do they have any helper apart from you. You are a person with a merciful heart, a heart which beats for distant people. Without a shadow of doubt, your heart has more right to love and beat for your closest.

O my dear, certainly the life which you are living is only for the useless and the jobless. These people do not have the capability, through any of their actions, to hide their shame and remorse from the eyes of mankind, until death comes to them. Thus, it is their death which then saves them from their misfortune, and from being exposed. Certainly you are not from them. O my dear, indeed you are walking the path to your grave. Despite that, you are not upset, neither are you distressed from life. So why are you facing the world like a person who is at despair from it, and wants to leave? If you do benefit from your second life and if your second life was going to restore all that which you had lost in your first life, then certainly I would have excused and pardoned you.

However, you know that indeed you were rich and now you became poor. You know that you were fit and well, and now you have become ill. You know that you were a nobleman and now you are humiliated. After all this, if you still consider yourself to be a fortunate man, then indeed this would mean that the earth is empty from unfortunate people.

Everything that you are labouring hard for in this life, only shows that you are in search of death. Why do you not gulp a drop of poison only once, and go straight to your death? This would be better for you than a slow agonising death during which you may forget your daily problems and difficulties, but your sins and crimes will increase. The punishment which God is going to give in the hereafter is going to be far greater than any punishment He is giving you in this world.

O friend, sufficient is for us the calamities of this life, which destiny brings to us. So why do we need to import new catastrophes for ourselves in our lives? Please bring forth your hand and make a pledge with me that you will become for me the same person you were yesterday. We were prospering before we parted, but when we did part, we became very unfortunate. Nevertheless, because we have now met, let us live again under the shade of happiness, dignity and honour, as we did before."

Then I stretched forth my hand towards him, and was concerned that he did not make any movement with his hand. Hence, I said to him, "What is the matter with you? You did not bring out your hand for me?"

He burst into tears and said "I do not want to be a liar, nor a person who breaks promises."

I said "What hinders you from fulfilling your promise?"

He replied "I am an unfortunate person. I have no luck or fortune at all."

I said "Indeed you had the power to become unfortunate, so why do you not have the power to become fortunate?"

He said "Because fortune is the sky and the misfortune is the earth. Descending to earth is easier than ascending to the sky. My foot has already slipped on the edge of a ditch. Now, I do not have the power to regain stability and I will continue to fall until I reach the bottom of that ditch. I have drunk the first gulp of life's bitterness. It is inevitable for me now to swallow the last remains of that bitterness. If I had never taken my first sip of this poison, then I would have a chance to change my wretched life. However, as I have done so, I have no choice but to accept my fate, and what God has decreed."

I said "This is not true. You can still be saved from your wretched fate by making only one truthful pledge. If you were to make only one promise, then you will achieve salvation."

He replied "To have a conviction is the sign of a firm intention, whereas I have become a man who is dominated and overpowered by life. I have no power or firm intention. Therefore, my dear friend, leave me alone, let destiny do with me whatever it wants. Woe, do not cry over your old friend after today, there is no use in crying for fallen sinners."

He burst out crying loudly, and left me in my place without saying another word. I had no idea where he went. So I left as well, carrying the heavy burden of sorrow on my shoulders, only God knew my pain.

***

As time progressed, the manager of the office could no longer bear his drinking partner, who's company he previously desired. Now he was a burden, he quickly took him out of his social circle. Following that, he started disliking his work, and discontinued his pay, having no sympathy for his desperate situation. My friend did not even shed a tear. Poverty meant he lost his house. The new owner did not give him enough notice, and threw him out after a few months. Thus he, his wife and two children took refuge in a vile room of an old house, nestled in an isolated alleyway.

After this, I used to see him either going to or coming back from the pub, and when he passed I would turn my face away from him. However, when I used to see him returning from the Pub in a poor state, I would draw closer to him, and wipe dust from his face, or clean off any blood which flowed upon his forehead. After that, I would take him to his house.

Like this, the days and the years continued to weaken his body and his mind, until he appeared as a walking shadow or a dream passing by for anyone who looked at him. He would walk the streets like a lost, insane soul, hardly feeling or sensing his surroundings. He could not escape obstacles in his way, until he came completely close to them. He would stop from time to time and roll his eyes, as if he was searching for something which he had lost, despite there being nothing in his hand.

Sometimes, he would catch sight of his clothes, which were now nothing other than sewn patches and torn rags. He looked at every passing face with hatred and suspicion, as if he was seeing an abhorrent enemy, despite not having any enemy or friend. Sometimes children would cling onto his shoulder, and he would gently remove them with his hand. He did not have any care for the infants, he removed them like a deep sleeper removing the hand away from his shoulder which was trying to wake him up. This was his state until his stomach became empty from alcohol, and the intensity of its need would shackle his head. Then he would go to the pub. There, he would persistently and excessively drink until he would return to his former state.

He remained in this wretched condition for a few months, until the following incident occurred:

His poor wife became penniless, and unable to obtain any provisions. She would cry helplessly when she saw her son and daughter cry before her. Their tears would speak the sorrow which their tongues were silent about. Distressed and desperate, she had no alternative but to send both of her children to houses for some domestic labour. This way, they could feed themselves and give her some sustenance as well. However, now she saw them very little. Neither would she see her husband, other than on nights when the police were watching him and this was not often. Therefore, she became a lonely woman in her room and had no one to take care of her. Her only helper was her neighbour, an old woman who would come and see her from time to time. Whenever she parted from her she was left alone to remember those pleasant days in which she had lived her life, loving the merciful, compassionate and never ending bliss between her honourable husband and children, radiant stars in contentment beauty.

Then, she would remember how the master became the slave, how the employer became the employee and how the dignified become dishonoured and disgraced. She would recall how the diamond necklace, perfectly and marvellously sewn together upon the neck of time, had been broken and scattered. After, the scattered diamonds would appear as discarded pebbles upon the dusty land, trampled on by shoes, hooves and the feet of other animals. She would cry like a mad lover forsaken by his beloved, until it felt that she had drawn very close to death.

Nevertheless, she never fostered any hostility in her heart for the person who was responsible for her ruins and the misfortune of her children. Her heart never wished any day to become displeased with him or to abandon and leave him. This was because she was a highly dignified, gentle and virtuous woman. Such a woman never acts treacherously towards her husband, who has been afflicted with catastrophe, but she looks at him with kindness and affection like how a mother looks towards her small child.

If her husband was ill, she would spend the night besides him staying awake. If he returned injured, she would plaster and bandage his wounds. On some nights, when the bartender could not find any money with him to buy alcohol, he would simply throw him out. He would return to his house in distress and in need, and severely demand alcohol. His wife, unable to find any alternative solution, would give him money saved from the household rations, or she herself would buy him alcohol to calm him down and give peace to his soul. She did this to show kindness to him, trying her best to save and maintain his remaining intellect.

As if her burden was not enough, destiny made her bear a new heavy load. She felt some breath of life and some movement in her stomach. She realised she was pregnant, and would be bringing a new member to this house of misfortune. Upon realising, she screamed loudly saying, "O my Lord, have mercy on me, verily the tumbler has

filled up, there is no more capacity in it for another drop."
She continued to endure the pains of pregnancy like an ill
woman, until the time came for her delivery. No one was
with her, other than her old neighbour. God helped her
with her affair, and she gave birth. However, straight after
she became severely ill with the fever of childbirth.

Her poverty meant she could not find a doctor who would
cure and treat her, as none were free. Hers was a town in
which the doctors did not feel ashamed to ask the patient's
family for their fee after the patient had died, even if it
was their treatment which killed the patient. Thus, it
would be impossible to find a charitable doctor here.
Death started to slowly draw closer, until the mercy of
God reached her, and she died. At that time, she did not
find besides her anyone other than her small baby who
was attached to her breasts.

At the same time, her husband also entered in his mad
state of addiction. He was in severe need of alcohol,
finding his wife so that she could give it to him. He
scanned his eyes around the room until he saw her lying
down upon her straw mat. He saw the baby girl crying
besides her, and presumed that she was a sleep. Drawing
nearer to her, he pushed the child away and started
shaking his wife aggressively. He felt and sensed no
movement. Suddenly, he felt a fearful shudder slowly
spread all over his joints until it reached his heart.

His senses returned and he slowly advanced towards her once again, staring at her intently until he saw the face of death staring at him with its gazing eyes.

Upon realising his loss, he recoiled in horror, and stepped back in fright and terror. However, worse was yet to come, as his ill thought steps landed unwillingly on his precious infant, crushing her chest and killing her instantly. She screamed one painful cry, after which she did not make a single movement ever again.

He ran out onto the streets like a rambling mad man, running frantically and screaming "Woe o misfortune! My daughter! My wife! Come back to me! Please take charge of me!" In despair, he hit his head on pillars and walls, pushing away all who came in his way, men and cattle.

Finally, he fell down exhausted on the floor, and started scraping the ground with his feet, sighing and screaming like a slaughtered animal. The people around him saw the agony and grief on his face, and rushed to console him even though he was a complete stranger to them.

For a brief moment, grief brought him back to his senses, showing him his terrible tragedy and loss. However, the shock was too great. Unable to face his dark reality, he quickly lost what remaining intellect he had left, and succumbed to madness.

Shortly after, he was locked away in a mental institution. May the Lord have mercy on him. May God also shower mercy on his innocent infant, unfortunate children and martyred wife.

THE REWARD

She was sitting at the corner of the lake so that she could fill up her water pot. The water was still and motionless, as if there was a layer of sparkling ice spread over its surface. She disliked to break this delicate and glossy mirror. To a woman, there is nothing more beloved to her than a mirror. She set her eyes upon it, and she saw upon its surface a handsome white face gazing back at her with a charming and entrancing look. She smiled back at him and he continued to smile at her. She speculated that certainly it was the face of her beautiful fiancé who was from the village. Her fiancé had always been infatuated with her.

She enjoyed this sight for a moment. Then, with fear, she realised that she was seeing another reflection in the water, a man who was not her fiancé. She became too frightened to look behind her, and drew her hand towards the water. She filled up her water pot and hastened to take it away.

The man who was standing advanced towards her and said to her, "O my respectable lady would you allow me to assist you with your water pot?" She turned back and discovered that he was both young and handsome. He was wearing good clothes, a stranger from the cities. She did not recognise him, and did not know that this land could give birth to the likes of him. She became doubtful about him and her face started to blush out of nervousness

and shyness. Not saying anything, she picked up her pot
and departed.

***

Susan and her paternal uncle's son Gilbert grew up
together in one house, like two similar flowers grow and
blossom together upon one twig. As a baby she drank
milk with him, as a child she played with him and as a
young lady she loved him. All times and eras had passed
by them, filled with mutual happiness.   Nevertheless,
neither of them had ever obtained any castles, gardens,
sofa sets, beds, horses, carriages, cups, casks, lutes,
stringed musical instruments, flashing gold, sparkling
diamonds, embroidered garments or decorated robes.

This was simply because both of them were two poor
villagers. However, both obtained happiness and bliss
from the rising and the setting of the sun, the coming and
the going of the night, the sparkling stars in the bright sky,
the greenery and the fresh vegetation of the earth, the long
stays upon the distinguished rocky mountain above the
motionless lake, the beautiful camping next to plants
above soft grass under the shade of trees full of leaves, the
rejuvenating humming of the birds, the songs of the
shepherds, the noise of animals grazing at day and at night
and from the crying of the waterwheel in the morning and
in the evenings.

Their pure and noble love brightened up sad hearts and
enlightened both of them.   This love illuminated dark

hearts and would become the feathers for broken wings. It would be the only comfort left when everything else in this world had come to pass, and the only satisfaction when everything else seemed to be lost. The woman of the lake was blessed with this love, until that fateful day at the lake.

***

A woman does not recognise her existence and her presence until she appears in the eyes and in the hearts of men. If, however, one area of the land had become empty from the faces that look and observe, or whether, from the corners of the ribs, the heart stopped throbbing and became desolate, then certainly her existence would be worthless in her eyes. However, if behind her a thousand eyes were looking, then certainly she would still glance at that star from amongst the stars of the sky which is adorning her with the sight of love. If, from any corner of the earth she hears a call of love, then she feels content over this new love and her heart fills up with happiness and prosperity.

Thus, this young woman returned to her house in a very happy state, her eyes were cold, she felt pride and a sense of self-importance. This was not because her new love had usurped her heart in place of her old love. Neither was this because her heart intended to attach her life with someone else other than of her fiancé, but because she had found in its way a new proof of her beauty which made her feel elevated.

She continued to visit the lake with her water pot, without any fear or doubt. She also saw that city gentleman mornings and evenings. He would greet her or he would smile at her. Either he would enquire directions from her or he would request her for drinking water. At times he would present her with a beautiful flower or occasionally whisper into her ear a gentle and sweet word. This continued until he finally managed to sit besides her for a little while beneath the shade of a lonely mountain. This moment marked the last pledge to her old life and the new pledge to her future life.

***

Sir Gustav Rostand had come to this village a few days ago in order to inspect his crops, as he did from time to time. He had built a beautiful palace two hours distance away from the lake, and enjoyed staying in it for a few days, before returning to Nice. However, this time, when he saw the young woman besides the lake in the mornings, he became attracted to her beauty. He nurtured his love in her heart and persistently whispered magical words in her ear. He adorned her neck and wrists with pearls and diamonds, and presented to her a beautiful sketch of city life, in its best and most beautiful form possible. He continued to give her very high hopes in respect to her present life and her future with him, eventually she submitted to him. She readily bowed down to his affections, how every woman kneels down when her guardians become careless of her. In reality, she had entrusted her destiny to the fangs of wolves.

***

A short distance away, Susan's fiancé Gilbert woke up at the same time he did every morning. As normal, he went to his cow and opened her rope. He then called Susan to take the cow with him towards the pasture and grazing land. She did not answer him, so he ascended to her room in the attic. He intended to wake her up, but did not find her there. He asked his mother about her whereabouts but she did not know anything more than him. He presumed that she had gone out to complete some jobs and would return later. He waited for her for a very long time but unfortunately she did not return. Now he had fallen into doubt and had returned the cow to its barn. He came out and started searching for her at every possible location, and asked her whereabouts from all people who were coming and going. He did not find anyone who could guide him to her. He stayed and inquired about her until the night shadowed him. Wearily, he returned upset and distressed, convinced that he was the most unfortunate person upon the face of the earth.

Upon entering his humble home, he saw his mother, withdrawn, standing head down in a dilapidated room, scraping the soil with a wooden stick. He drew closer to her. She raised her head to him and asked "Where were you O Gilbert?"

He said "I was finding Susan in every location possible but I could not find her."

She cast upon him a sight full of pain and tears and she said "O son it is better for you not to wait for her anymore after this day."

Gilbert shuddered and said "For what reason should I not wait for her anymore?"

She replied "Recently our neighbour, has come and informed me that, for a few nights, she has been continuously witnessing that Susan has been coming and going to the corners of the lake, in order to meet a strange gentleman from the town who is not from here. I am presuming that it is Sir Gustav Rostand, the owner of the fields adjoining ours, and the red castle nearby. She also told me that she saw Susan last night, after midnight, mounted upon a grey horse behind Sir Gustav Rostand, riding towards his red castle. Clearly she has ran away with him."

Gilbert screamed out aloud, his spirit was close to departing from his body, and he fell down, unconscious.

His worried mother remained sitting beside him the whole night. At times she cried over him and at other times she would wipe his forehead with water, until he regained consciousness at sunrise. Perplexed, his tired eyes examined his surroundings. Then he saw his mother, she had her head down and was crying and sighing. Seeing her, he remembered everything, and lowered his head with grief.

After a while he raised his head, and put his hand on his mother's shoulder. He asked "O mother why are you crying?"

She replied "O my son, I am crying for you and for her."

He said "If you are crying then cry over someone else besides me, I am not upset neither am I the one who is going to cry." He continued "Verily I loved this young woman because she had loved me. Now, my heart has become hard as a rock. There is nothing which is going to incline me to her anymore. Neither is there any return for me to her after this day." Then, he wiped from his cheek the last tear flowing upon it. He stood up and advanced towards his cow, took its rope and went with it towards the grazing field all alone.

***

Certainly that poor young soul had not been true to his heart. He did not forget Susan, neither had his heart forgotten the burning sensation of her love. However, his heart felt angry like a deserted lover, and he felt withdrawn from the extreme love which he had been clinging onto. When he reached the fields and sent his cow to graze in the pasture, he saw the sun slowly but gradually rising from its location, sending its scarlet sapphire rays all over the dark universe. This made the earth's layers brighter, flourishing its vegetation and soil. He liked the sight of this pure brightness upon the earth, and turned his eyes to examine its eastern and western hemisphere/ the horizon dazzling his eyes with its brightness. He felt that certainly the west had raised its own sun like the east had raised one. However, upon close scrutiny, he discovered that the sun was actually one big tablet, consisting of a round yellow mirror, playing the rays of the sun like how the rays play with the universe, this is why the light was extremely bright. He quickly moved his eyes back on himself and put his hand on his left ribs as if he was stopping his heart from escaping. This was because he had realised that this yellow mirrored tablet was flashing from one of the domes belonging to the domes of the red castle.

Now he realised that his heart had lied to him. Indeed, it was still glowing with love, lighting his forehead, and creating a raging blaze of fire which was tearing his heart into pieces. That raging fire penetrated into his heart the way death penetrates into life. Thus, his eyes began shedding countless tears, and he began crying and sighing very painfully. The winds in the air, the waves of the ocean, the vegetation in the fields and the cattle in the grazing land were all hearing and answering his cries. He cried until he heard the voices of the Shepard and the cattle, then he wiped away and withheld his tears. He lowered his head to his knees and in his imagination, with his pain and sadness, he went wherever God wanted him to go.

He remained like this day after day, the poor man could not benefit his soul anymore. His sorrows took him very far in his beliefs, and severely tormented him, morning and night. For anyone who saw him in the street, he appeared as an upset and distressed individual who had lost his senses and lived in emotional isolation. He wandered like a madman at nightfall and all hours of the day, in between bushes, lake sides and under high mountains. He bonded with the wild cattle like an old friend, but if a human was to draw near to him, he would run away from them like they were wild beasts. He would descend to the water springs with the deer and gazelles, and when they had departed he would also leave with them.

At times, his walking took him very far, and he would reach the gardens of the red castle without even noticing. When he would see the domes in front of him, he would get extremely frightened and scream out aloud. Then, he would turn back and return to his village without any care. A lot of the time, Gilbert's mother used to spend complete days in search of him, carrying his food in her hand. She would search for him at every possible location until she would see him either sitting in between stones besides the river bank or in the ravine. Then she would put food in front of him, as Gilbert had no clue of her presence. Then she would raise her hands towards the sky, in humility and distress, she would beg God through her tears and her sighs to return her only son. Then she would return to her village.

***

The night had not passed but only a little, as Susan was sitting down and looking at the lake from out of the window of her castle. She would glance at the bed of her daughter at one instance, and in the other instance she would look into the sky. It was the night of the full moon and she was saying,

"O the traveling moon in the midst of the sky, here I am seeing you complete for the twenty forth time. So is my fiancé Gustav going to return to me? O moon, is he going to see you with me the way he had before?

O bright star, what an excellent helper were you for my frightful nights, for my sadness and for my grief. So do you have the power to tell me about Gustav? Do you know his station and when is he going to come back? Are we going to meet soon so that your favour upon me would become complete?

Tell me about him, does he remember me the way I remember him? Has he safeguarded my pledge the way I have safeguarded his? Does he sit down with you from time to time so that he could ask you about me the way I ask you about him? If he does, then say to him that his daughter is extremely beautiful. The beauty of her modest smiles is like the smiles of beautiful women. Her fairness is like that clear white drop which is upon the lily flower radiant from the rays of the sun which is spreading light. O star, say to him that she does not call any other name apart from yours. She does not smile at any other picture save yours. Certainly, if he saw her, he would not even require any mirror anymore to see his own reflection. This is because he will see his face in her face, their similarity is like two dolls which have been created with one mould."

Susan used to keep on secretly talking to the moon like this until it descended towards the west. Then, she would bid her farewells to it, saying lovingly "O beautiful friend, I will see you tomorrow." She would advance to her daughter's bed, lean over and softly kiss her on her forehead with her evening kiss. Then she would go to her bed. The slumber of sleep would play upon her eyelids until her dreams would entrust her towards her hopes and happiness. Hence, in her dream she would see Gustav returned from his journey. She and her daughter would be waiting for him at the door of the castle, and Gustav would descend from his carriage to hug them both, pressing them to his chest very tightly. He would then continue to kiss them both, crying out of happiness and joy.

Whilst dreaming, she was shaken awake by an excited hand. Promptly she woke up to discover that it was noon and that the sun has ascended. She saw her maid standing next to her head laughing from happiness, declaring "O lady! Good news! My master is here!" Susan, in delight, said "Praise be upon you O Lord! Verily my dream has come true!" quickly, she ran towards her dressing room and changed her clothes.

She entered Gustav's room smiling and elated, holding their daughter in her hand. She saw him standing in the middle of the room, leaning behind his chair. She rushed towards him.

When she drew closer to him, her happiness to see him quickly became shadowed when she gazed upon his cold face. It contained no love or elation at her presence, and he was not even moved by her smiling before him. It certainly was him, yet she did not recognise his face, devoid of all affection, bleak and harsh. She stopped in her tracks, confused and disturbed, and nervously held out her hand to shake his.

Reluctantly, he shook her hand. Despite his daughter continuously smiling at him and stretching her arms towards him, he did not even look at her face. Then he coldly asked "Are you still living in my castle since that day?" It was his first word to her, filling her with terror, fright and confusion.

Perplexed, she asked "O master where would you like to see me?"

He replied "In this castle the way I had left you, however now I am thinking that you should not remain here after this day."

She asked "Why?"

He answered "Because my wife is coming here today and she would not like to see in this castle anyone who would distress her."

She felt all her blood race to her beating heart in an instance. The rest of her body felt numb, not wanting to scream or sigh at the catastrophe before her, merely staring at him, dumbstruck and disturbed. Then she turned to her daughter and asked "And what do you consider about your daughter?"

He said "O lady, she is not my daughter, neither do I have a son. This is because I have only been married for three days. Therefore, take your daughter with you and live with her the way you please. I have left for you this bag on the desk, take it and seek help from its contents in terms of your livelihood." After saying this, he left her and departed.

Susan did not glance at the desk even once. She walked on enduring these harsh words until she reached her bedroom. It was here that she burst out crying and said, "O misfortune, verily he has paid me the price for my dignity and my respect." After this, she fell down unconscious, and did not regain consciousness until night.

When she opened her eyes, she saw her daughter crying in the arms of her maid. The maid was also crying when she saw the infant crying. Susan hugged her baby girl and attached her to her chest for a brief moment. Then she stood up and went to her dressing room. She searched and took out her village clothes which she had worn three days before she entered into this castle. She had hidden these clothes from the eyes of people out of shame and embarrassment. She then took off her extravagant clothes and put her old clothes on. She did not leave any diamonds or any bangles around her wrists and neck, but took them off and threw them at her feet. She took hold of her child and left under the veil of the night. She was staggering in her walk as if she was walking upon uneven sand.

Susan had barely exited the castle when she stopped, still at that location where she and her daughter had been standing a couple of hours ago, waiting for her fiancé Gustav in her dream. At once from a distance, she saw a decorated carriage heading towards the castle, carrying Sir Gustav and his new wife. She closed her eyes and hid under the wall of the castle. After that she walked on her way.

***

Only God knew the weight of her grief and sadness. She had been hatefully thrown out from the castle, that castle of which she once thought herself queen. She was thrown out, cursed by that individual whom she believed had loved her dearly from all people and that she had given preference to. In that single second, this chaste young woman, a woman with a modest fiancé had changed into a prostitute with an illegitimate child. It became extremely difficult for her to return to her old house due to her shame and guilt. It was hard for her to face the two individuals who had done great favours upon her and loved her dearly. In return, she had been bad with them, and deceived them both. Every path was closed for her and everything between her and the entire world had darkened. There was no one who had mercy for her, in the world or in the heavens.

This is what she had been contemplating in her heart whilst anxiously walking under the walls of the castle, knowing no place or destination to go. As she was walking, she saw the head of her daughter swaying out of sleep. She ascended to a nearby hill top besides a flowing river, laid down her daughter on the grass, and placed her shawl on top of her. She then sat down besides her, and contemplated on what would be her outcome.

Certainly she was sitting in this location and verily the night was quiet. Every single thing was stationary other than the light of the moon, which was bursting into the atmosphere. The gusts of wind were creating waves upon the surface of the water. At once, she felt as if she heard near her, someone calling her name with a very low and a weak voice. When she looked, she saw a black thing lying down between two rocks nearby the lake, like a human being sleeping. She became frightened and scared. She then heard the same voice again. Considering the matter important, she rose and advanced closer towards the black shape.

There she saw a man dressed in poor clothing, lying down on his back and looking sharply towards the wall of the castle. When she scrutinized his gaze, she discovered that his eyes were glued to the window of her bedroom, where she used to sit every night in the castle. She trembled in amazement. She saw that he was holding a white thing on top of his heart very tightly. It was a piece of white paper. She kneeled over to see what thing he was pressing to his chest. She discovered that it was the sketch of her picture, and the being holding it was no other than her old love Gilbert, who was now very close to his death. He was persistently calling out her name with a low and dismayed voice, as if the voices of the deceased coming out from the depth of the graves due to being tortured. He was calling "Goodbye O Susan, goodbye O Susan."

At once Susan understood everything, and screamed out aloud, such a great scream that it echoed in the atmosphere. She said "Woe, verily I have killed you O my uncle's son." Then she fell upon his hand, she kissed it and started soaking it with her tears. She said "O Gilbert look, I have come. I am sitting at your feet. Please show mercy to me and forgive me my sin. Indeed, I have become a very sinful and unfortunate woman. There is none upon the face of this earth who needs mercy more than me."

Gilbert sensed and felt the melody of her voice. He went into a brief shock, then turned his eyes until they rested upon her. Suddenly, a single warm tear drop fell from his eye lid and landed upon her hand. Sadly, this was his last pledge with life, as then he passed away.

Just as my soul was ready to depart, that is the time when she had come.

When she had come, I could not give her anytime.

She came at such a time that in between her and me there was the river of death.

She cherished me with her meeting at a time when that meeting was non-beneficial.

***

For a while Susan remained seated beside the corpse of Gilbert, fulfilling that obligation for her uncle's son, for her fiancé and for her friend who loved her like no one had ever loved her before, and had died remaining faithful to her. Then when she come back to her senses, she remembered her daughter, who she had left asleep alone on the hilltop. Returning to her haste, she had decided in her heart what to do next.

***

Susan said "I do not know from amongst the people who I could entrust you to O my daughter. This is because your father has denied you and also the only individual who had loved me in the entire world has also departed. However, I do know about the merciful Lord who knows the secrets of the hearts. He sees the wounds of pain in the hearts of the distressed and He sees the agony and troubles of the unfortunate. So I am entrusting your affairs to Him and I am leaving you in front of Him. He is the most merciful one. O my beloved daughter, I do not have the power to remain alive for you. This is because there is no one from amongst mankind who would pardon me the sin which I have committed. That person who encouraged me and was a partner in my crime, even he will not forgive me. Therefore, I am going towards that heavenly world which is filled with justice and mercy, so that perhaps I might find someone there who could forgive me my sin. However, if I am convicted, perhaps I might find someone there who would be merciful to me.

O my daughter, I would hate my life to bring shame to your life, every time they will see you they will remember me, and attack you because of my sin. Therefore, I am leaving you all alone in this location so that maybe some kind person from amongst the people may show you mercy when he passes by you. He will take you with him not knowing a thing of your affair. You will live in his house, happy and prosperous. You will not know your father so that his affairs can put you to shame, nor will you know your mother so that her remembrance could trouble you.

O Lord! This weak and deprived child requires a merciful carer for her, because it has become impossible for me to stay besides her anymore in order to raise her, please be kind and shower your mercy upon her. She is innocent, pure and has no hand in that sin which her father has committed. Therefore, please show her mercy and cover her with the cloth of your eminence and of your favour. Originate for her someone who has a loving heart, a good house and establish for her a cherishing livelihood."

Then she began to take her clothes off from her body and covered her daughter's body with it. She wanted to save her daughter from the coldness of the night, leaving only one shirt on her own body. She left this on in order to veil her floating corpse once she had jumped into the water. Then she kneeled over the child with compassion. She kissed her on her forehead with a farewell kiss, encompassing all the love, mercy, compassion and kindness which was in her heart. Then she called out "O Mary, goodbye. O Gilbert, we shall meet soon. O Catherine (the mother of Gilbert), forgive me." After that, she jumped into the water.

***

Sir Gustav Rostand spent the first night of his honeymoon with his wife upon the attic of the castle, admiring and talking to one another. Both their eyes travelled over the green lands. At times they looked at the blue sky or the flowing river. They were enjoying their present happiness, and looking forward to their future prosperity. They were drinking wine excessively from every glass, until they got drunk and both passed out. Both became completely senseless of their surroundings, and neither of them awoke from their slumber until they heard a gust of wind blowing upon the minaret of the castle, and shaking the branches of trees. Realising this was a storm, they got up and went towards their bedroom in the attic.

In their bedroom, Gustav's wife was worried by the anxiety on Gustav's face. She saw him looking around in distress, as if listening to a strange voice. She asked "What is the matter?" He did not reply. Silently, he looked at the river from the attic window. In the light of the moon, he saw a child standing at the river side screaming "O mother! O mother!" in a high pitched voice and pointing towards the water. At once, both looked in her direction, only to discover that a half-naked woman was being tossed about in the midst of waves, plunging and drowning.

Gustav left his wife and started running towards the river, sighing "What a misfortune it would be if it is her." He shouted out to his worker to follow him, and they ran quickly to the locality of the child. He recognised immediately that she was his daughter, and indeed the drowning woman was Susan. Hence, the atmosphere darkened in front of his eyes. He instructed one of his workers to return the child to the castle, and search out the drowning lady. Then Gustav collapsed, traumatised and distressed. Many farmers, men and women, had gathered at the riverside. Some of them swam behind the swimmers and the remaining stood around Gustav, awaiting the mercy of God and His favour to be delivered.

The swimmers spread out at every angle of the river, the eyes and the hearts of people followed them. A giant war raged between them and the great waves. Sometimes, the swimmers would overpower, and at other times the waves would push them back. From a distance, they would catch sight of Susan's shirt, or feel her presence, and would advance forth in extreme haste, overpowering any great waves in their way. However, whenever they thought they had finally reached her, they would find nothing before them, apart from large waves pushing them back to their starting point at the riverside.

At times, the drowning lady became visible, but then disappeared. This continued until she completely disappeared from sight and was not visible at all. The swimmers followed her deep into the water searching and hunting. Then triumphantly, they resurfaced above the water, holding her between their hands. No one knew whether she was alive or dead, but they continued swimming with her. The people started praying for her and crying over her. The sky and both sides of the river started echoing with cries. Finally, the swimmers brought her to the riverside and placed her on the land, but she was already dead.

Very quickly after, the riverside become a place of mourning for the innocent dead. The women cried there over Susan's innocent death and the men cried over Gilbert's death.

***

After this day, Sir Gustav Rostand could not benefit himself anymore, and became helpless like Gilbert had been. His daughter became extremely ill due to the effects of this tragedy, and joined her dead mother after three nights. The love which his wife had in her heart for Gustav turned into enmity and hatred, she too left him and travelled back to Nice.

Gustav continued thinking about that sight which he had seen from the attic of the castle on the night of the drowning. The horrific memory of Susan did not part from him day nor night. Wherever he went, he would imagine that he was in front of the river and the waves were drowning Susan. He would see Mary screaming. At once, he would shout out "O Susan! I am here!" advancing forth in haste, as if he wanted to jump into the river to save her. When he was unsuccessful he would collapse with exhaustion, grief and regret.

At times, Gustav would wonder around, head down, until he would reach the outskirts of Leynes village. There he would see an old woman kneeling over a grave, crying and screaming. Realising this was the grave of Gilbert and the old woman was Catherine, he would recoil in fear and trauma, yelling "Mercy! Mercy! Forgiveness! Forgiveness!" A lot of the farming women would see Gustav collapsed in grief at places where they used to see Gilbert in. Accordingly, they would say "Verily, God has taken revenge for that poor martyr and for the death of that victimised, innocent woman."

The sight of the water would scare him more than anything, and his emotions would flare up, causing unrest. He would try to jump into the river, intending to drown, but the people passing by him would hold him back when they saw him. One fateful morning, there were no passers-by, and the people saw his corpse floating upon the surface of the river, in the same place where Susan had drowned. Everyone knew he had paid the price for his disloyalty to Susan.

Many years have passed by since this tragedy took place. The old women of Leynes and its surroundings still remember and cry over this ill-fated love. They narrate the story to their daughters and granddaughters, in order for it to serve as a lesson for them, if, God forbid, they were ever to be surrounded by evil people.

THE PUNISHMENT

One night from the nights of last summer, I had a dream. I descended upon a very big town, I did not recognise the town's name or locality, neither did I know in what era were its residents living in. Nevertheless, I walked along the streets for a few hours. I saw all kinds of different people in a large group, talking in many different languages which I could not understand. So, I speculated that certainly all the people of the world had gathered up in one town. I guessed that the people before me were all the people belonging to the past, the present and the future.

Thus, I continued to shift from one location to the other. At times I stopped and at times I carried on until I reached a very big building. I did not see any other building greater than this in terms of its prestige and its construction. A large crowd of people were standing all around the door of this huge building. There were soldiers coming and going there, walking in its courtyard and its veranda, holding their swords along with their sheaths. Accordingly, I asked some people who were standing, "What is this building and for what reason is this large crowd of people gathered upon its door?" They informed me that certainly this was the castle of the ruler and indeed today is the Day of Judgment, the day in which the ruler will issue his verdicts for people regarding their crimes. Not even a brief moment passed by, that a caller from amongst the people had called out saying, "Indeed the courthouse has opened, therefore all of you present yourself."

Consequently, the people entered and I also entered behind them. I sat down wherever I could find a place. Then I saw the ruler sitting upon a chair which was made out of gold. This chair was sparkling in the middle of the courthouse like how the sun shines in its horizon. Verily there was a man sitting on his right side wearing a sackcloth. Upon the ruler's left hand side was another man wearing a prestigious cloak. I questioned about them both. I recognised that certainly the one on his right is the priest of the church and the man on his left-hand side is the judge of this town.

I saw the ruler looking at a white piece of paper which was in front of him. He had his head down for a while, then he raised his head and said, "Let the criminals be brought."

Thus, the door of the prison was opened. On the left hand side of the prison, there was the courtyard. It felt like a cage containing lions in it roaring was opened. They came out, police officers who were dragging a very old man. It appeared that his bones and joints had given up due to extreme old age and weakness.

The ruler asked, "What is his crime?

The priest replied, "Indeed he is a thief, he entered the church, and then he stole a sack of flour from the church, which was collected for the distribution to the poor and the destitute."

Upon hearing this, the people cried out loudly and yelled, "Woe upon the sinful criminal, has he stole God's wealth from God's house?"

Then, witnesses were brought forth. The panel of priests gave testimony against him. Then the ruler discussed this matter with the priest briefly. Thereafter, the ruler declared his verdict, "This criminal should be taken to the slaughter ground, his right hand should be cut off followed by his left hand, then the rest if his body parts should also be amputated, and at the end his head should be separated from his body. His segmented body should be fed to vultures and the wild animals."

At once, that old man bowed down in front of the ruler and stretched out his trembling and weak hands towards him and begged him for mercy. The police officers hit him on his mouth and dragged him into his cell.

Thereafter the police officers returned, holding a young man who was about eighteen years of age. He was extremely pale and slim. He was trembling and shaking out of extreme fear.

When the police officers had made him stand before the ruler, the ruler asked, "What is his crime?"

The judge replied, "He is a murderer, one of your representatives approached him in his village to collect tax and requested the money which was due upon him. Indeed, he refused to pay in a very harsh tone of voice. Therefore, your representative shouted at him. In response, this man became extremely angry and in his rage, drew out his sword from its sheath and struck your representative which led to his death."

The crowd began to scream again shouting, "O what outrageousness and what an atrocity, indeed the one killing the ruler's representative is like killing the ruler himself!"

The panel of representatives who were the victim's team where brought forth by the police and they testified against the young man. For a short moment, the ruler lowered his head. When he raised his head, he said, "Take the criminal to the place of crucifixion, and hang him upon a branch of a tree, cut all of his veins and leave him until not even one drop of blood remains in his body." That young man screamed loudly and before he could explain himself the police guards surrounded him and took him back to the prison.

The police constables returned with an extremely beautiful young woman. Her beauty was comparable to an illuminated star had it not been for the cloud of sadness upon her forehead. The ruler asked, "What is her crime?"

The judge replied, "Verily she is an adulteress woman, a man from her family had entered her house only to discover that she was alone in her house with a strange man whom she loves and has decided to marry him before this day."

The crowd again broke out with a loud noise and in anger yelled, "Kill her, kill her, stone her, stone her, indeed this is a big crime and a grave deception."

The ruler asked, "Where is the one who witnessed this?"

Her relative entered and testified against her. The judge started whispering something into the ear of the ruler. Then, the ruler decreed, "Take this young woman to the ground of death as well, stone her naked until there remains not even one bit of flesh on her body or bones.

The crowd starting cheering and declaring how just and wise the ruler was. In joy they were praising and hailing the ruler, the priest and the judge.

The judge rose from his seat and the crowd also stood up with him. They left happy and overjoyed.

I also left the court behind these people upset and distressed questioning how strange and unjust these verdicts were, the ruler did not hear anything in defence of the accused, nor were these punishments proportionate to the crimes. I was amazed at the people due to their weakness and their surrendering in front of a powerful kingdom. I was amazed that they considered this government honourable and prestigious. They had entrusted all their affairs to it; whether it be just or unjust; whether it be mercy or dictatorship; the people had accepted the verdict.

I thought to myself, is there no thief, murderer or fornicator in this crowd? Are they free from sins? Is not there anyone here who could understand the excuses and justifications of the crimes committed by these individuals and then show mercy to them? Is there no one in this circle, who could observe their crimes with the same sympathy they would want for their own crimes? Is there no one present who would wish mercy and forgiveness for those standing in the dock as they would wish mercy and forgiveness for themselves?

Can it not be that the accused adulterous woman may not be adulterous? Can it not be, that the murderer had only killed in self-defence to protect his honour and his wealth? Can it not be that the thief had stolen only to feed his starving family and self?

Has not the ruler ever been committed to kill anyone even once in his life so that he maybe merciful to the murderers when he is investigating their crimes? Has the priest himself never obtained a coin unlawfully? If he has, then he should be less angry and more remorseful towards the one who has stolen the sack of flour from the church. If the priest has attained a coin unlawfully then he should be able to pardon that thief's crime as well.

Has the judge never slipped? Even once in his life, so that because of it, his anger over the criminal men and women could extinguish?

Who are these people who are sitting on these chairs ruling over the souls and hearts of men the way they please? Are they distributing good alongside evil between people the way they want?

Indeed, these people are not innocent Prophets, nor are they pure angels; nor are they holding a pledge with God from which they can investigate His people's affairs and decide their fate. With what right are they sitting in this gathering in a position of power? What jurisdictive authority do they have with which they have obtained this government and are ruling upon all people?

Who is this ruler? Is he not a very big tyrant or the son of a very big tyrant, who through his authority and power has taken the necks and the shoulders of people as a ladder to climb to the throne he is sitting upon?

Who is this priest? Is he not the shrewdest and the most expert in terms of robbing the weak and the faint hearted people?

Who is this judge? Does he not have the power to allow truth to prevail over falsehood? From where did the tyrants, the thieves and the unjust become the righteous, the pure and the good doers?

How strange is this, that a man has killed another man to save his wealth and dignity, and he is called a criminal? However, when the ruler decreed for the murderer to be killed he is called just. How amazing is this, that when a thief has stolen a morsel in order to fulfil his and his family's need, he is called a thief! However, when the judge ordered his hands to be cut off and his body to be mutilated, he is called a fair man! How strange is this, that a woman has slipped, perhaps due to the deception of men or through the influence of Satan, making people completely disliking her and not wanting to look at her anymore? But when they see her fastened upon some pillar naked, they pelt her with stones from every angle. Surprisingly, they are pleased with this sight and are happy at her location and at the retribution.

The way fire cannot extinguish fire, the second drop of poison cannot become the cure for the first drop of poison. Just like cutting off the right hand cannot become a remedy for the one who's left hand has already been cut off, evil cannot become the remedy for evil and a misfortune of this world cannot be wiped out by another misfortune. I kept on thinking about these things until evening.

I walked through a dark, frightful, open space until I reached the other end. There I saw a very scary scene which to this day haunts me. I saw the corpse of an old man drenched in soil. It had neither a head nor any other body parts attached to it. Then I saw his head and his body parts scattered all around him as if they were mourning and wailing over him in remorse. Then I saw that young man fastened upon a very dense tree as if he was one of its branches. All the blood drained from his body. After that I saw the young lady who had become a red lump of meat. Her head and her feet were not visible. There was a pile of stones which were drenched in her blood. I saw three dead bodies beside her in a deep ditch full of blood. I felt a black cloud descending over my eyes until everything turned black and I fell to the floor unconscious.

I did not regain consciousness until a great portion of the night had passed. I opened my eyes only to see a black thing slowly drawing closer to me. I became frightened at this sight. At once, I took refuge towards the trunk of a tree, I hid behind it. The dark figure kept on approaching me until it was right next to me. The dark figure, then lit a small candle he held in his hand. I discovered the figure was an old woman resembling a witch, dressed in tattered old clothes.

She walked on and then started examining the faces of the dead until she reached at the place of the old man. She knelt beside him for a moment and cried and wailed over him. She then walked towards his head and other body parts gathering them up, she placed them next to his corpse. She proceeded to dig a ditch for him under the trunk of the tree and then she buried him in it. After that she stood up upon his grave and saying her farewells she said, "O wronged man, O martyr, in the way of God you have died trying your best to save me and your troublesome grandchildren from catastrophe. Now you are in the guardianship of God. Verily your soul had departed from your body and your body remains in your grave. Without a shadow of doubt, you were the best husband and the best father. Your speech and your conduct was the most excellent. As a person, you had the noblest heart and spirit. Therefore, go to your Lord so that only He may recompense you, and beg Him to shower his mercy upon all mankind including even your murderers and those who did injustice upon you. Also, request Him to join me with you very soon. Thus, after separating from you, there is nothing which remains which could give me satisfaction other than the hope of meeting you."

I became very deeply touched seeing all of this and her crying made me cry. I was convinced in my heart that whatever she was saying was the truth; certainly, this old man was a martyr. I became determined to find out more about their story. I came out from my hiding place and walked towards her. Upon seeing me she became startled and frightened. Then she became calm as if she remembered that after the catastrophe that had fallen upon her, there is no bigger calamity than this.

I began my conversation with her saying, "O honourable lady, do not fear me, verily I am a stranger in this town. I do not know anything from the affairs of this town, nor of its residents. Indeed, I saw you standing upon this grave at this moment crying over the person who is in it. Hence, I felt sorry for you and I cried because you had cried. I would like you to share the pain in your heart, perhaps, I may be able to help you ease your pain." Upon hearing me her tears began to flow and she began her story;

"Indeed, my husband was never a robber or a thief in any one day belonging to the days of his life. He passed his days of youth and of old age labouring very hard. He was never reluctant even for a single moment in terms of striving for the livelihood for himself and for his family until our son had grown up. This was our only child. When he grew up he took away his father's responsibilities, which he could bear no more due to old age. Then, we were blessed through our son's help and life was good for a long period until our son tragically passed away. He died at a time when we needed him more than ever. He left behind, five small children, the eldest not even being ten years of age.

Certainly, by this time his father had reached extreme old age and the trauma of his son passing away had combined and he was unable to work. Therefore, we all landed into great distress and hardship. There was no one who could understand the hardship which we were enduring other than the one who has been afflicted himself with this kind of tragedy in life. It came to a point where we had nothing to feed our young with. We were in a dilemma! We knew that if the mercy of God does not reach us we would all indeed be destroyed. Thus, I did not see any other alternative but to resort to a scheme which all the troublesome and the poor take refuge towards. I started begging people for donations but I found no one kind enough to even give me a drop of water or a morsel of food. Neither did I find anyone who could guide me towards it. Due to this I found myself in tattered clothes and with a begging bowl in my hands. Then I returned home.

Only God knew what pain I had in my heart. I saw the little children awake and crying out of hunger. Then I saw the old man, my husband sitting with them drenching the ground with his tears. He was rubbing his palms together not knowing what to do or how to overcome this problem. If death had approached me this moment, then certainly that would have been easier for me to endure than this scene that lay before my eyes. My grandchildren were staring at my face as I entered and started circulating around me to see what have I returned with which would get rid of their hunger. But I had returned empty handed so I went to my husband and said to him; 'Certainly in the city's church there will be some stock for donation purposes and the senior priest has the authority to spend it on the poor and the destitute. If you were to go there and explain your need to him and request him to give you a little bit which will aid your need, then hopefully you shall return to us with that, which will eliminate the hunger of these poor children.'

My husband's face lit up with hope. He stood up and went towards his walking stick, taking its support, he walked towards the church until he reached it. He went towards the priest's room and stood in front of him. My husband presented his dilemma before him and wept at the priest's feet. The priest was unmoved and told my husband;

'Certainly the church does not do favours upon those people who have not done any favours upon the church before. On any day from amongst the days of your happiness and prosperity, you had never given any charity to the church. Therefore, mind your way, the doors of livelihood are open in front of you. If, however, the doors of livelihood do become tight upon you, then the doors of crimes are more spacious in respect to it.'

Thereafter, my husband came out upset and distressed. The sadness and despair of his life could clearly be seen in his eyes.

He descended from there and came to the courtyard of the church. Then he saw in one of its corners a sack of flour. A sudden idea occurred to him, he thought to himself that he should take it. This thought however, only came because of need and starvation, but he felt covered in shame. He closed his eyes and carried on walking until he reached the place where the sack of flour was and the thought of taking the flour reoccurred to him! He tried to get rid of his thought but he could not. He sat down beside the sack and thought to himself, 'I do not know anyone within the boundaries of this city and upon its land, a needier person and a poorer person than me. If taking this flour sack is a crime, then verily the priest has granted me the permission to commit this crime to safeguard my livelihood.'

He then lifted the sack of flour on his back and walked struggling under its weight. He had not yet left the church building and could feel the extreme weight of the sack. He thought he would not be able to carry on. His heart whispered, 'Remove the sack from your back.' However, in that instant he saw his grandchildren starving and crying from hunger. This spurred him on to continue walking home, every so often stopping taking support on a wall or his walking stick. This continued until fatigue overtook him, he struggled to breathe. His vision extinguished as he started vomiting blood and fell unconscious.

He remained in his place until some watchmen had walked passed him and they saw the flour sack beside him. By this time the priests of the church had created havoc, shouting and screaming, saying, 'The flour sack, the flour stack.'

They had been searching for the missing flour sack in all corners of the church, in the end they had given up on finding it. Thereafter, the priests had come out still searching for it everywhere until they met the watchman and then spotted their missing item. Not even an hour had passed by and the flour sack had returned to the church and the old man was put into prison. Then after that you already know what happened. O what a misfortune, my husband has been slayed unjustly. May the Lord have mercy upon me and my poor destitute children after him."

The old woman got up from her place and wiping away her tears with the corner of her scarf she cast a long look at the grave and said, "O my childhood friend, O support for my old age, farewell to you. Good bye O best husband. Goodbye O the best friend of friends, may God join me and you on the day of retribution." Then she turned back and left on the same path which she had come from.

In the depth of the darkness, her shadow had not yet disappeared, that I saw another shadow appearing exactly from the place I had seen the first. This second shadow was advancing towards me slowly and steadily. So, I hid behind the tree to see what this one would do. At this point the moon had become visible in the sky and it was sending its light upon this big ground. Thus, in the light of the moon I saw this shadow. It came apparent to me that it was a beautiful woman crying. In my entire life, I had never seen tears flowing upon such beautiful cheeks. For a moment, these eyes scanned all around until finally they landed upon the crucified corpse fastened upon a tree.

She walked towards the crucified corpse taking the rope in her hand. She then, untied its knot. She took the young man's body into her arms and placed him on the ground, standing beside it for a while observing it very quietly and peacefully as if she did not care. Then she burst out crying and wept, "O brother." She fell on him and started touching him. She began kissing him and stroked his hair and his forehead. She cried over him excessively in pain. She continued until tiredness had got the better of her. Her incessant crying stilled and she fell beside him like a twig falling to the ground. She did not move. The scene distressed me, so, I walked towards her until I reached her. I saw that she was struggling with her breathing but was alive. I sat at her head crying for her and praying to God for her until she regained consciousness. Thereupon, she saw me besides her surprised and said,

"O strange man, upon who are you crying?"

I said, "I am crying over you and upon your poor unfortunate brother."

She said, "Yes he was an unfortunate and a poor man, therefore O sir, cry over him abundantly, indeed he was the pride of the youth, the flower of life, the fragrance of life and the tranquillity of hearts. Without a shadow of doubt, they did injustice upon him when they killed him. He was not a murderer nor was he a criminal, but he was a man who saw his self-respect and self-honour being compromised by the hands of those who wanted to tarnish it. Therefore, my brother cut off that hand which advanced towards it, and he took revenge for himself, for his honour and for his dignity. If people had done justice upon him, then certainly they would have let him go having mercy upon him and upon his youth. This is because the one who defends his self-respect and the one who kills the one who intends to murder him cannot be a criminal."

I said, "O respectable lady, can you narrate to me his story?"

She replied "Yes, one morning in our village, a delegate from amongst the delegation of the ruler had come who would roam around towns and villages to collect tax. Thus, that deputy had passed by each house in our village until he reached our house. I was standing upon the door of my house and he looked at me with a lustful and an evil look that cast terror and fright in my heart. He then asked me about my brother. I took him where my brother was. When the deputy met my brother, and demanded from him money, my brother requested him for a few days to sell his stock. The deputy refused and stipulated that my brother pay immediately at that moment or he would take me as a security until payment was made. He then gestured to some of his troopers who surrounded me. Indeed, I have heard before this day the stories of those unfortunate young ladies who enter the ruler's castle in terms of security and deposit and after the payment they leave the castle despised, exploited, raped and impregnated.

I ran towards my brother and clung to him. My brother stood in between me and that man and said,

'You have no business whatsoever with this young lady, verily I am the one responsible for the money, therefore I should be taken in and not any other person. If it is security and deposit that you require, then take me as a deposit for my money until the money reaches you.'

The deputy said, 'It is inevitable upon me to collect the money or either take some security, and inevitably the security is going to be of my choosing. Therefore, if you refuse, then you would have to forfeit your life.'

My brother became enraged with anger and a stream of sweat poured down his forehead. I had never seen such anger within my brother before this day. Then my brother said to him,

'Then let my life be sacrificed for my pride, for my honour and for my values.' Saying this he withdrew his sword and struck it removing the deputy's head right off from his body with one swipe. My brother remained standing there and did not run. Drops of blood were dropping down from his sword until the soldiers had shackled him up, and taking him as a captive imprisoned him in the prison.

O dear, this was his life and this was his death. Thus, if I am crying, I am crying over a courageous young man. I am crying over a young man who had integrity and honour. He was the best of brothers in terms of mercy and decency."

Then she asked, "O sir, are you going to help me to bury him before day light comes between me and him? This is because verily I have become weak and helpless. I do not possess the power to do anything."

I stood up towards the tree and started digging up a ditch near the tree's trunk next to the grave of the old man. I buried him in it and hid him within the grave. The young lady advanced forth towards the grave and kneeled over besides it for a short while, having her head down, she sat quietly. I did not know whether she was crying or whether she had fallen unconscious until eventually she got up from that location. Thus, I saw the soil of the grave which was drenched with her tears. Then she spread out her hand towards me and said, "Thank you very much O respectable person. Indeed, you have helped me at a time when a very few people find any helpers." After that, she left and went on her way. My eyes followed her until she disappeared out of sight.

I returned to my thoughts and to myself. I realised that the corpse of that stoned woman was still at its location. Her sight was distressing and I thought to myself that indeed what could be a greater act of kindness which I could hope for reward from God on the Day of Judgment, then to bury this poor woman in the ground. Therefore, I started digging up for her a ditch next to the graves of the other two martyrs. Then I put over her my garment and holding her in my arms, I laid her down in her ditch. While I was in the process of throwing soil over her, I felt some movement behind me.

I turned back to find a young troubled man standing, enveloped in a black cloth. Only the whiteness of his face was visible. He was the first to start conversation with me, he said, "O good man, who is the person of the grave whom you are throwing soil over?"

I replied, "It is the young woman who was stoned. I saw her corpse being unattended to in this ground, therefore, out of compassion for her, I decided to dig a grave for her."

Then the man said, "O kind man, between me and this young woman, there is a bond, would you allow me to say my last farewells to her before this soil comes between us."

I said, "Yes certainly, it is your affair, you may do as you please."

I Moved aside. He drew closer to the grave and knelt on top of the grave. He started talking to the deceased lady. I felt as if the stars in the sky and the winds in the atmosphere were re-echoing his words. He continued with his discussion until his heart attained tranquillity. Then he stood up and started putting soil over her until he had buried her.

After that he turned towards me and said, "Most certainly God has thanked you for this act of kindness which you did for this young lady who was wronged. You covered her up whereas people had completely disclosed her body. You safeguarded that which the people had disrespected. May God reward you good over what you did, and may He also do a favour upon you the way you had done favour upon her."

He was about to leave but I promptly stopped him and asked him, "Did this young woman die unjustly the way you are saying?"

His lips moved generating a small smile and he looked at me with a peaceful and a content look and said, "O kind man, yes, if she was not then you would have not seen me here in this moment of time standing in the corner of her grave crying. I am the man whom they had slandered and accused her with. I am confident enough to declare to you the way I am going to declare to my Lord on the day when I am going to stand in front of Him, highlighting the injustice which was done upon her, certainly she is exempted from the sin which the people had accused her with. Without a shadow of doubt, she was purer than the dew which is upon a flower. She was cleaner than a clean drop of water. Verily I loved this young woman ever since we had been small, we played with each other. She likewise had loved me. Then we became adults and our love also blossomed. We pledged to be loyal and sincere.

Then I sent the proposal of marriage to her father. He accepted my proposal with happiness and with prosperity.

When there were only a few days remaining for our wedding night, her father tragically passed away. Thus, we realised that we inevitably would have to wait for one full year. When one year was almost over I had to go to the judge of the city regarding some issue relating to her inheritance. However, when the judge saw her, he fell in love with her and sent a message to her paternal uncle.

Her uncle had become her guardian in her affairs after her father's death. Her uncle was a very greedy man. He was amongst those people that if they saw a sparkling coin on the other side of an ocean full of blood, they would jump in it.

The judge had expressed his desire to marry her to her uncle. Her uncle overwhelmed with joy and excitement, not delaying a moment accepted his offer and went to the young woman to share the good news.

She was saddened and said to him,

'Verily I do not have the power to have two fiancés' in one time.'

Her uncle did not care about what she had said and told her, 'Soon you shall get married with him, whomever I choose, willingly or unwillingly. You do not have any authority over yourself, verily all the authority is mine in matters concerning you.'

Not even a few days passing by, all the preparations of her wedding were complete and the day of her departure was fixed. Before the sun could set on that day, she gathered all her belongings from her house, encompassing her clothes and her jewellery and then left under the stars of that night, not knowing where was she heading, where she was going and which path she should adapt. Verily her uncle raised the matter of her running away to the judge. The judge promptly sent his helpers and his guards in search of her at every possible location. Some of his guards had seen her sitting behind some walls and went towards her. She became scared when she saw them. She left her bag at that place and ran away from them as fast as she could.

At that moment, I was just returning to my house. At once, she saw me and then she threw herself upon me and said,

'Verily they are following me, if they find me they will kill me, have mercy on me so that God may have mercy upon you.'

Her situation had completely stressed me out as I then took her to my house and I hid her in one of the rooms. Not even a moment passed by that her uncle entered. Behind his uncle there were the judge's guards. Her uncle was searching for her with extreme determination. I denied having seen her at all but he did not believe me.

He started slamming open all the doors until eventually he had found her and shouted, 'Here is the young adulterous woman and this is her companion.'

I swore to him every kind of oath belonging to the faith that indeed she is free from that slander which they were accusing her with. Regardless, they did not believe me. Her uncle ordered the guards to capture her, I got in between them and her. Then, one of them hit me over the head with a heavy blow due to which I fell down unconscious upon the floor.

I did not wake up from unconsciousness for an hour. When I did, I felt a very strong fever burning my body and became bed bound for a few days. Whenever, I had gained slight consciousness, I would picture that scene which I had seen. This would cause me to fit and I would fall unconscious. This continued until I attained the mercy of God as I became and felt better. A few days after my recovery, I had the strength to come out of my house. I came to know all this innocent lady had gone through. So, I have come here to bid her my last farewells and to wrap up her dead body and bury it, I am not going to enjoy the taste of life after her until I meet with her."

Then after that, he casted a final look at her full of sorrow, sadness, burning passion and remorse. After that he went on his way.

Not even a little while passing by, I saw the moon disappearing. The entire atmosphere became quiet, and the ground became scary and gloomy. Then I climbed upon a hilltop, I could see the three graves from here. Then with my large scarf I covered myself up, and rested my head on some rocks and thought to myself,

Is there no just person or a compassionate man left upon the face of this earth anymore? If the earth does not contain neither, does that mean that within the heavens there is also no just or compassionate being?

That religious guide sinned because he became miserly towards that poor old man over one coin which was amongst his possessions. This one coin however could have got rid of his and his families hunger. Due to this, the man was forced to commit the crime of stealing. Then the thief was penalised for his stealing. However, the cruel man was not penalised for his harshness and his ruthlessness. If it was not for the cruelty of that cruel man, then they would have not been stealing from him.

Regarding the ruler, indeed he sinned because he sent his deputy to abduct a chaste woman who did not want to compromise her honour, because of this her brother was forced to confront the deputy which led him towards the crime of killing. Accordingly, the young man was punished for his crime. However, the one who caused this crime to be committed in the first place, has been exempted from punishment.

The judge had also sinned. This is because he intended to force a young lady who did not love him to marry him. Thus, because of this, she ran away and due to her fleeing she was penalised. Regardless, the judge was not punished for his tyranny or injustice. Like this, the criminal became exempted and the exempted became a criminal. Moreover, ironically, it is the culprit judge who has been given the authority to penalise the innocent.

So, after this day, is the sky going to fall upon the earth? Is the sky going to continue to brighten the earth through its stars ever again? Is the sky going to send rain again?

Then I turned towards the place of the slaughter where these inhabitants of the graves were killed, my sight landed upon the ditch which was filled with blood of these martyrs. I saw the reflection of the star lighting up the surface of the bloody trench. I raised my eyes towards that star only to discover that it was the planet Mars. It was blazing with fire and rage as if it was the hearts of these people demanding retribution. I stared at it for a while. Then I saw it descending from its height slowly and gradually. As it was descending, its body kept getting bigger and bigger. It continued to mount down until there remained between it and the earth what appeared like a mile or even less in distance. Then I saw it having a shivering fit and it suddenly turned into an angel of punishment, fire was blazing out of its eyes and from its nostrils. With its wings and other body parts it was gliding down. It kept on descending until it landed upon the head of the tree that was shading the graves of those martyrs. Then its wings triggered off a shake so severe that all corners of the earth had shook and lit up. It started speaking with a voice like a thunderbolt of lightning in the horizon. It said,

"Look, these people are repeating those acts which they used to do before. Look, this earth has filled up with evil and mischief once again. Look, there remains no vicinity or location which is pure and righteous where an angel from the angels belonging to the heavens can take refuge towards. Look, the powerful have become more powerful and the weak have become weaker. Look, the flesh of the weak is entering the bellies of the rich continuously and the ones at the forefront are not going to bear this anymore and the ones who are behind them are not going to suffice upon this anymore.

Look, the poor are dying of starvation, they are not finding anyone who could be kind towards them. Look, the distressed are dying, they are not finding anyone who could help them with their problems and with their adversities.

Look these are the rulers, indeed they have breached the trust and the pledge of God and have broken it. They have put away the swords which God had given to them to establish justice and the truth. In place, they have drawn out other swords which are not used to establish the law of God and neither to serve humanity. They are walking along with their own swords, in search for their own desires and lusts. They keep on going until they obtain it.

Look at these Judges, certainly they have become greedy and tyrant. They have made laws only to exercise their hunting and oppress the weak. They arrest whoever they want under their order, as there is no one to question them.

Look at these contractors of religion, verily they have become the contractors of the world. They have converted their places of worship into the houses of thieves. They collect for it, stealing wealth from people. Then they become stingy with it, not even giving a little to the poor and the destitute.

Look at these people, verily they have become the helpers for their rulers over their desires and fantasies. Indeed, these people have become the supporters for their judges over their injustices. Certainly, these people have become the assistance for the contractors of religion over their stealing.

Let the wrath and the punishment of God fall upon them all, whether it be the rulers or the ruled, or whether it be the king or its subjects.

Let the thrones be overturned. Let the places of worship be destroyed. Let the courts be broken down. Let the towns, villages, the mountains, the elevated and lowered places all be destroyed. Let the earth be drowned in the ocean of blood drowning in it men, women, old people, the children, the good, the bad, the criminals and the innocent all. God has not done injustice upon them but it is them who have done injustice upon themselves.

The angel of punishment did not complete his supplication yet, that the ditch of blood started to boil and heat up, like on the day of the supplication of Prophet Noah, how the stove boiled and heated up. Then the blood over flowed from the ditch and travelling with a fast current, it spread in the earth creating a fast-flowing flood of blood. At once, the earth appeared as an ocean of blood which was spreading and scattering fast. It was destroying everything which came in front of it, whether it was the green lands, the cattle, the castles, the cottages, the animals, the humans, those who spoke and those who did not, all were destroyed.

Then I felt the ocean of blood was gradually rising higher and higher until its waves had hit the top of the hill where I was sitting, I screamed out.

I woke up from my sleep and from my dream. It was the morning of the day, 28th of July 1914. At once I heard a caller screaming, "The War has begun." (The 1st World War)

THE VICTIM

(THE STORY)

Margaret Jowita became an adult. She was poor and had no money from which she could buy herself a husband. She did not find any man who could sell himself to her without any money, nor did she find anyone who could fulfil her needs and to safeguard her chastity. However, by all means, it was inevitable for her to live. She did not find any way of earning a livelihood other than by compromising her respect. Thus, she took her self-dignity to the markets of misfortunes and grief. Some dealers fixed a mean price for her. Despite disliking this occupation, she sold herself and became from amongst the bearers of loss.

Indeed, her beauty became a misfortune for her. If she had been ugly, perhaps she would have found someone from amongst the people who would have shown mercy to her but beauty is the merchandise of profitable trade. The possessor of beauty does not endure the power to obtain anything from the people if she is poor and deprived, other than to sell herself.

For this reason, the burdensome woman became hateful towards all men. She swore that she would beautify her appearance in order to take revenge from them as they have exploited her dignity and her chastity.

She fulfilled her promise, the way a loyal person fulfils his pledge. She starting living with men but she did not love them. She became extremely happy when she destroyed them and their wealth without any remorse. She used to see under her feet the tears of those who used to cry with extreme joy and pleasure and she used to say,

"Woe upon you O the assembly of men, I did not ask you but only one bread in the afternoon and one bread in the evening with respect and honour, but you refused to give them to me. However, when I asked you through indecency and through vile behaviour, you gave everything you possessed, all your wealth and all your properties, knowingly and with your free will in the state of happiness. How small are your hearts and how corrupt are your characters?

Indeed, the most inferior within the society and the one considered the most humiliated in front of people had the power to marry me; he could have had my body, my heart, my life without any money in exchange of fulfilling my needs and safeguarding my respect. However, you did not do this! Now, all your respected and honourable people are bowing down upon my feet the way a despised, a humiliated dog bows down next to his master's dinner table. Though, they do attain from me more than what that dog receives.

You loved your wealth abundantly and you rejected to marry anyone other than a wealthy woman, so that you can mix your new wealth with your old wealth. However, today, spend all your money on a woman who is a prostitute, who will give you neither any money nor any love. Spend all of your silver and gold until remains neither for you any new wealth nor any old wealth."

***

Margaret appeared in the sky of Paris as a sparkling star which spread its light, dazzling the eyes and enveloping all corners of the atmosphere with brightness. The intellects started circulating around her like a honeybee hovers around a flower. Gold and silver started flowing in front of her rapidly like a fast river in the evening sun. Respected faces had kneeled in front of her and the elevated foreheads had stooped at her feet. The necks of all men together had appeared in her hand as if she had tied them in one rope. She would to shake one corner of the rope, causing the men to shake, and when she withheld the rope in a stationary position the men also became stationary. Her state with them became like a master dealing with their dog. She never quenched their thirst completely and neither did she satisfy them totally. However, she did not keep them hungry lest they become unresponsive towards her. She used to create hope and desire within her lovers until they assumed that now their luck had drawn them close to her and there was no distance remaining between him and his desire so much so that that if he was to stretch his hand towards her he would obtain it. Promptly she used to cast him away like a poor thirsty being is refused water at his mouth. However, when she would learn that now he has become hopeless, has had enough and that he intended to go away with full conviction of not returning, she would send him a ray from the rays of her sweet intoxicating smiles, there after he used to return to her willingly and being submissive.

In this manner, this young naked hungry woman who needed a morsel yesterday and did not even have rags to cover herself with, became the Queen of Paris and the Sovereign of its throne.   Like this, she became the possessor of the bridle connected to all the men and she became a pain for the women of Paris. She became that bright star that the eyes gaze upon.   She became that hidden secret which even the intellects used to reflect upon.

This was what the people knew about her. However, what she knew about herself was that whatever the people had given to her in form of gold, silver wealth, money, houses, flats, properties, horses and carriages, were not even equal to, nor compensated for even one tear from amongst the tears she had shed on the day when she had sold herself. Certainly, these diamonds, these gems, these clothes, these crowns were given to her by men so that she could wear them so that she could please and satisfy their desires the way an owner of a dog enjoys seeing a beautiful collar around his dog's neck which the dog himself gains no personal benefit from. Nevertheless, she acknowledged that she had sold herself without a price and without any gain.

Whenever she was alone, she remembered that these hearts which were flying around her were flying only over her beauty and not for her. Her speculation was that if she was deprived from this beauty even for a second, then all people around her would flee inevitably and she would be left alone, abandoned in this world. As then no heart would show affection to her and neither would an eye cry over her. Thus, she used to cry, weeping in pain. She used to consider herself to be a troublesome lady like them because she lives with them and yet has no love for them. She was living between a nation who didn't have genuine love for her but fake and false love.

Whenever she passed by the servant quarter of her castle in the morning and evenings, she saw her servant sat besides his wife and children. She saw his show of a lot of love, affection and sincerity towards them and likewise they in return were showing the same compassion. She too wished, if only she too could have this love and compassion in the form of a husband and children. She wanted this more than anything in the whole world.

People saw Margaret never allowed a married or engaged man to enter her house. People assumed that this was due to her selfishness. They used to say that she is a greedy woman who does not love anyone other than him who is completely sincere to her. Only if the people had known her reality and the secret of her heart, then they would learn that she was an extremely hurt woman who was torn apart with sadness. Verily the world had deprived her with the blessing of marriage but she still safeguarded and acknowledged its value. She hated to give pain to another lady.

Indeed, some people had recognised her affairs of her private life, and stated that she has given money to poor young girls as a dowry two or three times and with its aid they got married to whom they wanted. However, people did not believe this news and said, "Indeed a thief can never become charitable and certainly the spring of good deeds can never gush out from the heart of an adulteress women." Nevertheless, the truth was that she did do this and she had done so numerous times.

This was the heart of Margaret and this was the secret of her heart. She herself was destroyed, despite that she was not pleased with her destruction. She was a fallen woman yet, she disliked to see other women falling in society like her. Only if it was within the power of a fallen lady to return, after repenting and re-establishing her state amongst the hearts of men again. Only if they could wipe out whatever they had committed before from amongst the indecency through reconciliation, then this would have been the most superior thing for women in terms of repentance and in terms of disposing their affairs. Nonetheless, it was the society which made her fall, and it was the society which stripped away her veil of honour which she used to wear. If now, she was to request her veil back, society would refuse to return it to her. Consequently, she had to now continue living in a fallen state whether she liked it or not!

A few years passed and Margaret became ill, so much so that she became bound to her house for quite some days. After that her illness increased. Therefore, the doctors suggested that she should go to the Pioneer in California to use their baths and spas so that through its water and air she recovers from illness. She travelled there alone with her maid. There was an old rich gentleman called Duke Mohan at Pioneer with his daughter. His daughter was also ill. She was suffering from a severe chest infection as her father wanted to cure her illness. However, he could not find any cure for her and tragically she died in his hands. He buried her there and remained there for a few days. He kept on going to her grave and kept on crying profusely.

One day he was returning from her grave and Margaret was walking ahead of him on the path, it was Margaret's second day in Pioneer. The old man was astonished and amazed when he saw her. He thought to himself that verily God had sent his daughter back from her grave or that He has sent him her duplicate, her identical so that he can give his heart contentment. This was because both of their faces looked the same. In a surprised and astounded manner, he approached her and held the corner of her scarf. Then he stared at her face for a long time. Margret was also surprised at this strange occurrence and she asked him, "What do you want?"

He said to her, "O lady do you grant me the permission that I may kiss your hand?"

Margaret extended her hand towards him, she did not know what he wanted and what pain he was enduring in his heart. Then that old wealthy man kissed her hand and then he apologized to her for his strange behaviour. That old man then walked besides her telling her his story and the story of his separation from his daughter, and the resemblance between his daughter and Margaret. She felt sorry for him and through his pain she also became upset. The old man saw her eye wet with tears. Thus, he fell upon her hands and starting kissing them and he thanked her for the generosity which she had given to him through this tear in his unfortunate time. They continued walking until both reached their destination. The old man bade his farewells and departed after seeking her permission to meet her from time to time. After granting this permission Margaret went to her room.

However, when she was alone in her room, she starting thinking about that young poor woman, and how death had taken her away from her father's hands, and that neither a doctor nor an herbalist could save her from dying. Then she feared over herself that she too was ill like the that young girl who had died. She thought to herself that verily, if she was to die like her, she would not find next to her, a father expressing pain and crying over her. This thought and this concern pained her heart severely. She cried over this for a long time locking herself to her room and not coming out.

Duke Mohan kept on coming and going to Margaret's room after this and would sit there for a long time. He obtained love and comfort from her and became happy in her company. Whenever the flame of pain flared up in his heart, he would obtain peace and tranquillity just by sitting with her. He became so attached that he did not have the power to part from her. Margaret liked to see that an old distressed man who has lost his daughter found tranquillity and patience every time he looked at her face. In return, she also showed kindness to him and gave him love which he had never received before and that she also loved him like she had never loved anyone else before.

Not even a few days passed by, she gained recovery from her illness. Her splendour and beauty had returned upon her beautiful face. The stunning smile and laughter had reappeared on her lips. Her staying at Pioneer for a long period had been beneficial for her and she liked it until she felt the cold winds of the winter coming through so she decided to return to Paris. This decision was hard upon the Duke. He knew if she was to go back, he will not be able to meet her the way he had at Pioneer. This was because then she would be in large crowds and gatherings amongst her companions and friends. He stayed with her all night before her journey. He talked to her for a very long time in which she agreed to leave her former life, the life of deception and the life of living with other people and to live in a house which he will provide for her along with providing her provision and sustenance. In return he only asked for one thing, which was that she grants him the permission to come and meet her from time to time. They both travelled together to Paris.

From that day forward, her lifestyle changed. She started living in the castle which Duke had provided for her. She stopped meeting a lot of people like she did before. Sometimes days used to pass and people would not see her leaving her house. When she did come out, she used to embark in her carriage alone, without any companion male or female. When she walked her path, she read a book or a magazine. Whenever she walked past people whom she knew and recognised, she would not look at them. However, when her sight did land upon any one from amongst them, she smiled briefly, no one used to see this other than that person. Then she used to continue her journey until she reaches the Shanzelize Park. Then she would descend from her carriage and walk towards the forest where she remained for some time. Then after this she used to return to her mansion.

When it was night time, she used to go to the theatre alone or she went with her bodyguard. Thus, she used to spend a lot of her time watching the entertainment on stage. The audience did not distract her when they and those who were obsessed with her, kept on staring at her. Also, when she was performing herself, she was not distracted by them as she used to continue with her story and with her act until the end.

Not many days had passed that the news spread amongst the people that Margaret's state had changed and her life had changed. She has attained contentment with her new life, the life of peace, quiet and living alone. She was pleased with herself. No one could dominate her anymore. The greed that the people had before for her had lessened and all their desires had also finished.

Then the people started to investigate about the reasons which led her to change her state. They speculated every possible reason for this other than the real reason behind her transformation. The actual reason was the tragedy of Duke Mohan's daughter's death who was the spitting image of Margaret and had suffered a similar illness. Indeed, this touched her heart very deeply which caused her to change her life in respect to what it was before. Thus, she became hateful towards men because they were the cause of her destruction. She hated her downfall more than she did ever before because this was what led her to her illness. She was not upset anymore over the fact that she was being deprived from other people's wealth. This was because she was living on the wealth which the Duke provided for her. She was living in such prosperity that not even a greedy person could ask for more. Sometimes she used to ponder that, indeed her life was connected to an extremely old man who does not want anything at all from her but only to see her. She used to consider her life like the virgin pure girls who are blessed under the honourable shade of their parents. She liked this and having this thought made her feel happy. This was because, it was this honourable life which she longed for and cried excessively over before this day. She had admired having this life before.

***

Now, the days of autumn had passed and the days of winter had approached. The icy cold and bitter winds had increased and Margaret's illness which was hidden had returned and her chesty coughs which contained blood in them also returned. She was in severe pain. When she was in pain, she stuck to her bed and did not part from it. However, when she felt better, she went outside for fresh air in the morning and evenings. Sometimes she used to go to the theatre at night to lessen her pain. She would remain there for an hour or two alone in her gallery box and then return to her abode.

Whenever she used to go to the theatre, she used to always look at the gallery box which was next to hers. There she used to see a young man who was dressed like a gentleman and had noble etiquettes. He used to look at her secretly too from time to time. Whenever she was looking down that's when he took a glance at her and whenever she looked at him he would look away. However, whenever their eyes met each other

178

simultaneously, his face used to blush and his forehead used to sweat like he had sinned greatly which there is no expiation for. However, she never felt concerned over it because she did not see anything new in this other than that young man was extremely patient and silent, and that for a long time he would lower his head and his gaze. The cloud of distress was scattered over his face. The thing that astonished and amazed Margaret greatly was that from the whole audience, he was the only one who would cry when he saw a tragic and a heart-breaking scene on stage. This was because she knew that verily young happy men who are flourishing in their youth and health do not care if some real tragedy took place, let alone an imitation of this tragedy upon stage.

One night Margaret was alone in her gallery box. The night was extremely cold and at once she underwent a state of severe coughing. Then her symptoms increasing, so much so that she was going to fall off her chair due to her weakness and illness, that she felt a hand which was holding her hand. She took support from the hand and without paying attention to whose hand it was, she managed to reach her carriage and embarked on it. After a little while she felt better. Then she turned back to thank that gentleman for his favour but saw no one there but in the distance, she saw a person walking away. Nevertheless, she recognised him as his appearance was etched in her mind. She was astounded. When she reached her house, she felt a shivering fit of a fever which spread all over her body. Then for a few days, she remained in her bed and did not part from it until she felt better. Her maid came to her with the visiting cards which those young men had left when they had visited her during her illness but she did not read even one of them. Then her maid said, "There was one young man who used to come every day or twice a day to find out your well-being. He did not mention his name neither has he left a visiting card. Indeed, he became stressed out every time I told him that you were still in bed and in severe pain."

Margaret asked her to describe him. The maid described him but she did not recognise him. Margaret was completely amazed at this gentleman's actions and wished to see him, so that she could thank him for his exclusive sincerity which she did not see from any from amongst the people before. Then she instructed her maid to inform her whenever that man comes again to ask about her once more.

Not long had passed that the man returned. Margaret was sitting in the balcony facing the road and so, she saw him. She recognised that certainly he is that young emotional man whom she saw in her neighbouring gallery box in the theatre. Also, she discovered that it was his hand which had come out to help her on the night when she had undergone her illness. Promptly she instructed her maid to go to him and bring him to her.

The man became extremely nervous upon this invitation and he was very close to declining the offer. Then he realized that Margaret was sitting upstairs and became extremely shy. He walked behind the maid until she got to Margaret's room and leaving him there departed.

He entered her room and gave his greetings to her. He was sweating profusely and could not speak. Margaret stretched her hand towards him. He held her hand and gave it a very long kiss. Margaret came to know about that secret love he held in his heart for her. She was well-aware of the secrets found within kisses. Then she granted him permission to sit down. She began asking him about himself, which family was he from and the reason for looking after her. She kept on smiling at him to soften the tension between them and to get rid of the apprehension that he was feeling in his heart. Then he told her that verily he is a stranger in Paris. He had arrived with a delegation twenty days ago, from his town Nice so that he could spend three months here. His father had granted him the permission to do this to have a change in the air and water and to revitalise him. Then after that, his instruction was to return back to his town.

She asked him, "Did you find this place beautiful?" He remained silent for a little while. Then he looked at her hopelessly and said,

"No dear lady."

She asked, "Why?" He was unable to respond for a long time and put his head down. Margaret repeated her question to him.

Then he said to her, "O my respectable lady, do you grant me the permission to say everything which is in my heart?" Before he said anything, Margaret had already sensed what was in his heart, and said to him,

"Say whatever you please, however do not express to me your love and the passion that you have for me. This is because verily I am an ill woman, I do not even have the power to endure this life which is free from problems, let alone enduring a life which is encompassed with love and pain."

His face turned pale and he stretched his hand towards his eyes where he wiped away a tear and said to her, "O my dear lady, this is what troubles me, this is what makes me cry and this is what has made my life unbearable ever since I have come to Paris! Ever since I have laid my eyes upon you, I fell in love with you at first sight. I started querying about you and I found out everything about you. I even found out that verily you are now living a life for a couple of months where no person of desire will be granted his yearning and no hopeful person would be able to fulfil his expectation. Thus, if I had any bad intention with you, that also perished other than that sincere love which I had for you did not extinguish. Then after that, I saw you at the theatre and I saw this yellow veil which was woven from the hands of illness upon your beautiful face, this turned my love that I had for you into mercy and kindness. Now I cry over your illness more than which I used to cry over your love. Now all that I wish for, from

God is that, in my lifetime I see you happy, in tranquillity and in a healthy state. May you receive your portion of happiness in your life in abundance. After this, I do not have any greed for anything anymore, unlike the avidity of those lovers and devotees. Thus, now I am standing in front of you, not to express my love and my emotions to you, but standing only to request your permission to come to your doorstep, so that whenever I come I may enquire about you from your maid. Then after that, I will be on my way. You will not see my face neither will you be aware of my coming or going."

Thus, a shivering fit penetrated through her body parts, this was a fit other than the fit she used to feel when she was feverish. She felt that verily she was listing to a song of love which she had never heard before this day from the mouths of men. Thus, she looked at him with a sight which other than God no one knew. Then she said to him, "O dear I give you the permission and I am very thankful to you. In fact, I grant you the permission to visit me whenever you want upon the condition of coming as a helpful friend and not as a fornicating lover. This is because indeed I need a sincere friend and not an obsessed lover."

She drew out her hand towards him. From this he gathered that verily she has given him the permission to leave. Then he kissed her hand and left in a very happy state. Her eyes followed him until he disappeared. Hence, she fell upon her cushion which was next to her and cried, "O Lord please have mercy on me, verily I fear that will start loving him."

Certainly, she did start loving him in a state that she did not know. This was because the fear of falling into love itself is an indication of love. Nonetheless, she felt extreme happiness in his love, a feeling of which she had never felt before. Every day she welcomed him in her house. She became highly attached and friendly with him and became extremely excited with his conversations. She revealed to him all her secrets just like a friend discloses to a friend. She told him the story of her past life and her present life. She did not lie about a thing neither did she hide any matter from him. Then the matter accelerated to such a degree, that she started missing him if he got late to meet her even for a few seconds. Then, there came a time when he could not visit for three days because of some issue arising. She was traumatised with his absence greatly and her speculation and thoughts ran wildly in every direction. She came to realize that certainly this kind of pain and sadness of him not coming and this type of conjecturing of hers did not arise before. She became deeply saddened as her heart started worrying due to fear and terror. At this point she realized that she was standing upon the edge of a ditch and there was not option remaining for her other than to jump into it. She remained awake for a very long portion of the night and endured her heart's fear and its pain until the morning burst forth.

Arman came on the fourth morning. He found her lying down on her bed and because of her crying and being awake, her eyes were red. Arman became worried seeing her in this state and said to her, "Possibly you have been awake all night or maybe you have been crying my dear? I see in your eyes the effect of either one of them."

She said, "Both of them O Arman."

He said, "Why, has a new issue arisen?"

She replied, "O friend, sit beside me so that I may talk to you for a little while, as this maybe the last discussion between you and me. Then after this I might not see you and you may not see me." Thus, Arman became troubled and concerned. Terror and fright penetrated his mind and his tongue. He did not have the power to say anything as he fell next to her unnerved and powerless. He began looking at her face like how a criminal looks at the face of a judge waiting to hear the verdict. She leaned towards him and said,

"I have recognized you O Arman. I have seen within you a generous man, who loves me more than he loves himself. You are a lawful friend in whose heart kindness and mercy have united with the sentiments of love. You have taken refuge towards me, towards an ill woman, at a time when people ran away from me due to my illness and you stayed with me without having any expectation at a time when people had boycotted me because their yearning has ended. In my heart, I have been hiding your love and your esteem which I have never had for anyone before. I became blessed with you with such a blessing that I have never felt anything like it in my life. However, God had written for me misfortunes in the divine tablet, all the way from my mother's cradle till the final resting place in the grave. He did not intend me to enjoy this blessing of having you for a long time. He denied it and took it away from me very quickly. For a few days now I have felt that pure dignified sentiment of love which existed in the depths of my heart, which I used to seek solace in for my calamities and for my catastrophes. Now this sentiment has changed into another sentiment. This new sentiment I do not like as I can see this leading me towards my downfall and ruin. Indeed, my heart has deceived me from time to time. Sometimes I deny it and sometimes I grant it. When you had gone away from me for three days, I realized and felt the pain of your absence. This stressed me out a great deal and had me extremely worried. This stress has overshadowed all my sentiments and senses. If you want me to say this, then I will say that it is this stress which has caused me to cry a lot and it has kept me awake. Woe to me, I have found out that certainly I have fallen in love and verily this sentiment has woken up my heart. This feeling makes me stand up and makes me sit down. Indeed, this is love and devotion.

I spent all night yesterday thinking of a way of salvation from this great trial which has afflicted me. I did not find anyone who could save me from this other than you. Thereby, O Arman, I ask you in the name of friendship and love, over which we had made a pledge yesterday, but in fact, with the name of those merciful tears which you shed caring for me, that you stop coming to see me from this day onwards. If you can, please travel back to your family tonight and do not ever return to see me after this. I will establish patience within myself from you until God favours me to become despaired of your love."

Then she looked towards him awaiting his reply. He became still and his face became pale. Becoming like a statue, his eyes were staring at her in a frozen state, the likes of which when the eyes are staring but cannot see. In a very difficult manner, he just about managed to move his lips and said in a very quiet manner as if it was the voice of his heart. "If it is love, then what is your fear O Margaret?"

She said, "A great trial and punishment is scaring me, which I am expecting from God, due to those sins and mistakes I committed in the earlier days of my life. Verily God has written for our assembly of fallen women in his decree, that we play around with the hearts and minds of men, and that we put them through various problems and several punishments. We continue to do this until God becomes enraged for the men and feel's a sense of honour for the men, and He retaliates by punishing us through love, and then we experience all that punishment ourselves which we had inflicted upon the men before us. We suffer harms and sorrows throughout our life and we die as unknown women whom no one cares about. There is no one who gives the news of our death and there is no one who cries over us. Thus, this is what I fear. Therefore, before I can see this I would like to die. O Arman Indeed I am not accusing you of cheating and deceiving, you are greater than that in my eyes. However, I do know that you are here in this town only for an appointed term. Then after your time lapses you will travel back to your family then you will not return to me after that and if you refuse to go back and decide to stay with me then your family will come between you and your decision. This is because your family are honoured and dignified people who are protective over you and will want to safeguard your respect. They will never allow a prostitute woman to stain you with shame and disgrace.

Thus, you will not find any way of redeeming yourself from them and you will have to give in to their verdict. Then you will see me standing staggered and in pain and I will be seeking you but I will not gain you and I will want to have patience over you but I will not be able to do so. I have even thought that if I return, after being rejected by your family towards the shelter of that honourable old man, who had done a very big favour for me, he will even reject me by punishing me for my breaching of his trust and being unthankful for his blessings. Thus, in that position I will not able to find another alternative but to return to my former life, the life of sins and immoralities, the life of sadness and pain, the life which I despise like the earth dislikes blood. I will become trapped in an everlasting punishment and in a long calamity.

Verily I know, O Arman, that you indeed love me a lot and I know that you will suffer a lot of pain parting from me. However, I do know that in the path of mercy, an honourable heart manages to endure pain. So, endure this punishment because of me, indeed you have more strength than me to withstand this pain and agony. I will supplicate to God that He grants you, patience over my pain, and that He gives me patience and contentment of the soul after you. I pray that God gives you, patience like the patience that He will give me. I hope that God showers his mercy upon us both collectively."

Thus, he did not have any answer for her in respect to these words other than him getting up from his station trembling and unsteadily walking towards the door of the courtyard. He was forcing and dragging himself towards it until he finally reached the door. He stood upon the doorstep and turned towards Margaret and cast one last longing look at her, like a dying person who looks at his family in the last moments of his life. Then he said, "Goodbye O Margaret!" and walked away. He had not even disappeared that Margaret got up from her bed, crying and shaking she ran towards the door intending to join him. Then she came back. After a split second, she got up and ran again once more after him but, her integrity had brought her back. She returned to her bed and began to cry, began to scream and wailed loudly. Then she started pacing her room like an upset woman who just had a death in the household. She was screaming "Return him to me. I do not have the power to endure his separation. Soon after him I will die."

She was in this state and suddenly she heard a loud scream from the direction of the garden. She rushed out to the door of the house and saw it was Arman who has fallen down in front of the door step unconscious. Consequently, she raised her eyes towards the skies and said, "Let it be whatever God intends." Then she placed herself over him and hugged him. Then she kissed his lips. That kiss was the first kiss in which she had felt the true taste of life within her. Arman felt the kiss and woke up. He hugged her to his chest. So much so, that, if he had died after this mere hug, he would not have cried over not having anything else from the blessings and the happiness of this world.

***

Winter had passed and Margaret's illness and sickness had also come to pass. She recovered from the virus and became blessed with his love. Now, her only task was to sanctify this relationship before God. She proposed to Arman that they both leave Paris, its crowd and its fast lifestyle and go towards a summer residence of their choice in a quiet area. Thus, he accepted her decision and both travelled together in search of a suitable place until they reached a village called Bougival. This was a parish from the settlements of France which was two hours away from Paris. They found a small house built on a hill top and located behind a big green mountain, and a beautiful clean reservoir was flowing beneath it. As if the originator of it had made it for the two of them. They rented the house. Margaret had transferred all her luggage and all the necessary things from her house in Paris to their new residence.

They both started living a life which was full of contentment, pleasure and happiness. Never did the clouds of sadness spread over them. Never did any assumptions neither any dangerous thoughts ever distress them. They would begin their day climbing on top of the mountain or descending from it to the lower ground. Or they would come and go on a small boat and cruise upon the lake. Or they would sit under a thick tree which used to shade them from the noon's heat and seam them both together to itself. Or they would lie down upon the carpet of grass in the open space talking to one another. They used to enjoy the beautiful sight on the corner of the lake. They used to attain bliss from the beauty of the water, the sight of the vast lands; the valleys, the forests, the places of grazing, empty spaces, ravines, caves, the clouds and the illuminations in all its forms and colours. They would enjoy the alternating and moving shadows and enjoyed looking at the peaks of mountains which looked like they were connected to the sky. They would adore the pebbles and rocks which were scattered around the reservoir as if they were the waves in that pool. They would admire that battle which took place every day between the light of day and the darkness of night. The light would attain victory at the break of morning, then at the end of the day the night would prevail over light. At nightfall, both would return to their house happy and content with their life.

Both continued living in prosperity and happiness until a whole year had passed. They had the power to obtain from the hands of destiny anything they wanted. Then after that the world had woken up for them. Woe is upon the fortunate people who wake up after being asleep. The money which Arman had was nearly coming to an end. Therefore, he wrote to his father requesting that he sends him some money so that he could remain in Paris for another term, pretending to be ill, in need and unable to travel. He would do did this from time to time. However, he did not receive a reply to his last letter. This upset him a great deal. Every day he would go to town; to the Toren Hotel. This hotel was where he used to stay before he met Margaret. He used to come here to ask about any post that may have arrived for him, each day he returned disappointed and distressed.

However, when he would reach Bougival and see Margaret in front of him he would become happy and smiled like he did not have a problem in the world. However, Margaret could see beyond the empty smiles into the depths of his heart. She shared her concerns with him saying; "Do not worry O Arman concerning the money. Indeed, I have with me an amount which will suffice us both for another few years." However, what she said was not true. This was because the Duke had stopped sending her money and deprived her from his care ever since he found out about her story with Arman and that she had deceived him and had breached his trust.

She was in debt and owed a great sum of money to the clothes and jewellery merchants. Now the debtors had started to ask her for their money after finding out that Duke had abandoned her and had taken his hand back from her. She had not reflected on the consequences of what she had said to Arman!

Arman did not like her offer and disliked to live off her money. He refused to live with her with the wealth which is other than his own. He intended to travel to Nice, so that he could bring back money from there. His intention to travel had upset Margaret and had scared her. She knelt in front of him and started requesting mercy and compassion from him. She started to beg him not to go. In fact, she had pleaded with him greatly not to go. Thus, Arman agreed and cancelled his trip. He became content with that thing which he should not have become content with. If it was not for the yearning of love and the burning tears, he would have never agreed to her request. Secretly he had decided he would bequeath his share of inheritance to Margaret, to compensate for her sincere loyalty and love.

Margaret was left with no choice but to start selling the diamonds and expensive treasures she had. She began selling them bit by bit in order to pay off her debt and also to maintain the expenses of the house. However, Arman did not know all of this, and both continued living like this for a few months.

One day a worker from the Toren Hotel came to them announcing, "Verily your father has arrived in the Hotel, and he is eagerly waiting for you."

***

When Arman came face to face with his father (who was called Duval) he said to him, "O Arman certainly you have been lying to me a lot. You had never lied before this, neither have you ever deceived us before this. I was pleased with you and I wanted you to have the best life ever in respect of other people before you. You have torn up with your own hands that beautiful veil of honour and modesty which was always over your face. You have started living your life with a prostitute. The status which this woman has; all the people including this woman know and acknowledge that she is a discarded and fallen down woman who has no prestige whatsoever. She is the leftover and the remains of rambling and erratic people. She is that chewed up bone of that dinner which is open to all kinds of people in the mornings and in the evenings. I have had enough of you, now stand up this instance and get ready to travel back with me to Nice. I am not going to leave you here after this day for another moment."

Thus, Arman raised his head towards his father and said to him in a very confident and peaceful voice, "I do not have the power to do this O father!"

His dad stared at him and said, "This is the second sin which you are committing. Do you not care for me at all? Do you not have any shame that you are rejecting my decision over a fallen woman who has no respect? She is playing with your mind and she only wants to strip away from you your wealth and honour. She wants to destroy your past and your future."

He said, "No father, indeed she is not playing with me neither is she deceiving me. In fact, she loves me so much that she has never loved anyone like this ever before. I believe if I were to leave her she would die. If I were to leave her, I would be committing such a big sin that its regret would not part from my conscience till death."

His father replied, "Women like this deceive men like you, filthy women like this do not have the hearts to love with. But they have the tongues with which they trap men with and they put a curtain between men until everyone from amongst them considers himself to be the most loved one, the most fortunate one to her in respect of the others."

Arman said, "Before this day, it maybe she lived like that, however now she does not love anyone else other than myself. In fact, she does not know anyone else besides me. Now she lives a life of an honourable lady, rather a life which is purer than a lot of honourable women. This is because a sincere friend who has sincerity for a friend is purer than that wife who cheats on her husband. I fear that if I leave her, that fire of despair in her heart will reignite and return her to her former life of sin, wickedness, misfortunes and punishment, which I had saved her from."

Arman's father said, "What do you think, this is the only good deed left for good people? That they rectify and correct dirty women?"

Arman said, "This is a better thing to do, bringing back a woman from the life of sin and wickedness towards the life of purity. This is because the respectable people of this day and age boast about how they have ruined the lives of respectable women and how they slowly but gradually misled women towards destruction and immorality. To rectify a character of a bad woman is better than misleading a pious woman."

Duval said, "Certainly you have become really merciful O Arman."

Arman said, "Why should I not have mercy for a poor, ill, young woman who does not have any one in this world who could look after her from amongst her relations and friends? Her illness has moved into her chest which does not finish neither does it part from her. However, from time to time she does feel relief from it and sometimes it triggers off again and she undergoes severe pain at times, and sometimes she fears that pain returning. There is no relief for her in these two states other than pondering over this blessing of love as she sees herself recovering through this. If I was to lose her, she will lose everything in life, her sadness and calamities will increase and her illness would further escalate until her remaining life will also come to an end. O father, please leave me here with her for another year or two so that I can lessen for her, her misery and it may be that these are the last few days of her life, after that I will return to you with a contented heart, with a clear conscience and pleased with myself over my actions and I will only shed tears of sadness and not the tears of guilt and regret; I will feel happy and peaceful every time I will think that I had never broken my promise to her and that I had never deceived her."

Duval put his head down for a while as though he was coming to terms with grief, then he lifted his head and looked at his son with love and mercy and said, "O my son how can I travel without you? Is it not enough for me that before this day I have also been enduring the pain of your separation? I have left your sister behind also who is also very anxious over you, she cries night and day and is extremely eager to meet you. Everything which you have said in your defence, will not save me nor you on the day when people will talk about your absurd behaviour. Many people have already started talking. They have said 'Indeed Arman Duval, the descendant of the family of Talleyrand is living with a prostitute in one house.' So please return to your senses O son, and seek guidance from God, He will guide you, do not let your emotion overpower your intellect and leave living this low life with this woman. The only people who live like this are the people who have no courage unlike you. The only people who live like this are those who have no honour and no house, whereas you have both, dignity and a house. I am leaving you now alone so that I can go to do some work. Use this time to think over this, perhaps your lost understanding may return. Then I will return to you after a while to hear from you those words which I expect will cure me and will quench my thirst."

Then his father left and walked towards a coffee shop which was near the hotel. Thereafter, he went to visit his friends whom he knew in Paris. He took a very long time visiting them. He did not return to the hotel until the night had come to pass.

He saw that Arman was still sat in his place. Then he asked him, "What have you decided?" His answer was within his tears which were flowing upon his cheeks. Arman knelt in front of him and started beseeching for mercy and kindness from him. He started sharing the secrets which he had been hiding before.

He was saying, "By God O father, if I could see any way to live in this worldly life without her, then I would definitely leave her, listening and obeying your command. However unfortunately, I know that verily if I were to do this, then I will be placing myself in harm for I fear that I might go insane or lose my life. I do not know what my outcome would be? The misfortune of going mad or the adversity of losing my life will inevitably strike me. If there was anyone before me who had the power to eliminate his desires from his heart, or had the power to wipe out what destiny had written for him from the troubles and difficulties of love in the pages of decree, then I would certainly follow his way of how he did it. However, the calamity which has struck me requires my death. Therefore, I have no say in this, neither do I have a plan to overcome it. This lady has become a part of my soul, she is the life in my body. If you find it compelled to take me, then take my lifeless empty body with you."

His father placed his hand on his shoulder and said to him, "Stand up now O my son, and go back to your life but return back to me tomorrow morning, so that I may complete my conversation with you, and I hope that tomorrow you will be in better state than today." Thus, Arman left upset and worried.

He was walking like an insane madman. He could not see what was in front of him, neither did he have any sense of his surroundings. He continued in this state until he saw a Hackney carriage. He mounted it and travelled in it to Bougival. He reached his home late and did not see Margaret in the balcony of the house waiting for him the way she used to.

He entered the house and then entered her room. He saw her bowing down over a table which was in front of her, it felt that either she was sleeping or either she was extremely worried. She sensed him entering and stood up startled. Arman noticed the letter which she was pressing in her hand. Arman assumed it was a letter from Mr John Phillip which he used to send her time to time. Mr John Phillip was a young gentleman and the son of an elite wealthy dignified family. He used to love Margaret in her former life and would spend a lot of money on her. However, when she broke connections with him, this did not deter his hope. So, he kept on sending a lot of letters to her declaring and presenting his love in them alongside with money. He offered good hope and faith to her to return to him and a request to connect her life with his. However, if it ever came to her attention, that the letter was from him or she recognised the handwriting she would rip it up. Arman did not care about the letter and went to her and gave her a kiss.

She said to him, "O Arman what happened?"

He said, "My father wants me to go back with him but I refused and in front of him I cried a lot, I did not move from my decision. Verily he has ordered me to come back to see him tomorrow, but I am not intending to do so. This is simply because the distress of tomorrow will not be any better than the misery of today. My heart is motivating me to rebel and to stay here rejecting his order because I know that certainly I have passed that age where sons are in need or dependent upon their father's advice. Also, because I do not know anyone from amongst the people who could write in my destiny a fortune better than the way I can write for myself." Then he began narrating his complete story; the account with his father to her until he finished. Then he looked at her and found her bowing down and standing in a quiet state. He discovered that her face was pale and withered as if the cloud of death was hovering upon her. He asked, "What is the matter O Margaret?"

She said, "I feel severe pain in my head. I want to go to my bedroom." Thus, Arman held her hand and took her towards the bedroom. Arman gave her some drops of her medicine and she felt a little bit better. Then she slept in her bedroom a sleep which was fitful and frightening. Long nightmares and distressing dreams were disturbing her. In the morning, she said to Arman, "O Arman, I think you should return to your father the way he has ordered you to do so and that you beg him for mercy and love, perhaps today you might attain that which you were unable to achieve yesterday. Verily I will not become satisfied with myself neither will I be content with my life until your father becomes happy with you." She kept on persisting until he listened to her. He got up and went towards his clothes and got dressed. Then he walked towards her and hugged her tightly, pressing his chest with hers as if he did not want anyone to take her out of his arms. Then he kissed her and said to her, "I will see you in the evening O Margaret." She did not respond to his farewell until he was far away from her. Then she said to herself, "If only you do come back the way you say." Then she fell on her chair crying and screaming.

Arman kept on walking on his way until he reached Paris. Then he went to the Toren Hotel. Thus, he did not find his father there. However, he found a letter which his father had left there for him. In it he had instructed him to wait there for him until his return. So, he stayed put and waited until he came. Half a day had passed.

Indeed, that black cloud which was veiling his father's face yesterday had lessened. Arman walked towards his father and greeted him. Then his father said to him, "O my son, indeed I have been thinking about you extensively all night and I feel that I have been very harsh on you and that I have upset you significantly. I pondered over your issue with a narrow mind, whereas it was crucial for me to contemplate over it with an open mind. Certainly, the circumstances of young people are unlike the situations of old men and women. Young people have specific circumstances whether they are honourable or disgraceful. There is no differentiation between a vulgar person and a king."

So, I grant you the permission to stay with her the way you please O my son and you can live with the woman whom you love, just the way you want. However, this would be upon your pledge and promise to me, to return to me on the day when the relationship comes to an end. Regardless of whether your relationship ends with her whilst she is living, or when she dies. Indeed, I am not worried for you in respect of her, but I will certainly be worried over you in respect of a woman other than her."

Consequently, Arman was overcome with happiness and joy. He bowed down upon his father's hand and started kissing it. Arman was soaking his father's hand with his tears and he was saying, "I promise you O father, that I will certainly do this, this is my pledge which I will never go against neither will I break it and with you will be the decision, if you see me after this day lying or the one breaking a promise."

Then Arman stood up intending to leave. Thus, his father asked him, "Where are you intending to go?" He replied, "I am intending to go towards Margaret, to inform her of this great news, and to relieve her heart from the terror which has gripped it since yesterday." His father shook but Arman did not notice. Then Arman's father turned his face away from Arman, to allow time for the tears which were hovering in his eyes to dry up. Then he turned back facing Arman and said, "O my son, please stay with me today, most likely I will be going back tomorrow, and I do not know when I am going to meet you again." So, Arman stayed with him one full day until night came. Then he sought his permission to leave and go to Bougival. Hence, his father gave him the permission. He said his farewells to him and came out. His father's eyes followed him until he disappeared from his sight. Then, he allowed the tear to run free which he had been withholding uttering, "May the mercy of God encompass you O poor child."

***

Arman rushed home to share his excitement with Margaret, until he got close to Bougival. He became frightened to see that the house was extremely dark and quiet. There was no ray of light in it neither did he see any shadow in there. He walked towards the door only to discover that it was locked. Then he placed his ear upon a crack of the door but did not hear any movement. Then he started knocking the door hard. He was shouting out for Margaret at times, and at times he was shouting out the maid's name but no one replied to him. Then Arman thought to himself, 'perhaps, she has gone to her house in Paris for some matter and her maid has also gone with her and that inevitably they will be returning now.'

Thus, he sat down upon a rock which was facing the door of the house waiting for her until one portion of the night had passed and she did not return. Then he forced himself to also go to Paris, to find her in those places where she could be. But he became afraid that if he left for Paris she maybe on her way back and he would miss her. So, he remained sitting in his place at times and other times he would get up. At times, he stayed put and at times he started pacing. He thought of every possible danger of loss and tragedy that could have occurred, other than the thought of her deceiving him and showing disloyalty to him. He remained in this state of distress until the light of morning spread. He became distressed at the thought that, inevitably something has happened to Margaret, and it was crucial for him to get to her. It became absolutely vital for him to see which condition she was in. Due to being anxious and being awake all night, fatigue overtook his body and mind in such a way that he could not think straight anymore.

Subsequently, he set off way to Paris like a drunken person falling all over the place until he reached Margaret's dwelling place. He saw the watchman of the house who had woken up from his sleep and was standing next to a tree with an axe. He was cutting down its branches. Arman asked him about Margaret. He replied, "She had come here during night yesterday, her maid was also with her, she was holding a big bag, she went in the house and stayed there for an hour and then she came out. She was wearing a dress from amongst the wedding dresses and giving me a letter said, 'When monsieur Arman asks about me give him this letter.' Then she embarked upon her carriage with her maid and went."

Arman asked, "Do you know where she went?"

The watchman replied, "I think I heard her say to the driver when she was embarking on her ride, 'Go to the house of Mr John Phillip.'"

Thus, Arman froze like a statue and his colour changed to the colour of death. Like lightning, that letter which he saw in her hand the day he returned to her after meeting his father, started circulating around him. The watchman left Arman in his place and went to his room and returned with the letter. Arman took the letter off him with shaking hands and opened it. He swiftly glanced over the text and had understood everything which was in it in his first glance. Then Arman's body started to tremble severely and he started stepping back a step or two towards the door of the mansion. Then he rested his back upon the door and returned upon reading the letter which was composed of the following words,

'This is the last thing between me and you O Arman. Do not think in your heart to ever meet me again. Do not ever ask me the reason. I do not have any explanation with me other than this is what I have decided fit for myself. Goodbye.'

Thus, Arman's eyes were glued on to the letter for a while. He did not raise his eyes from it neither could he read a word from it. He stood like a statue. Then the watchman returned towards his tree and continued cutting its branches. The watchman was singing when he climbed up the tree, he was enjoying its tune despite of not understanding its meaning. Suddenly he heard a heavy object falling upon the ground.

He threw his axe and ran towards the sound. He saw that Arman had fallen and was covered in dust under the doorstep. The watchman became extremely frightened and presumed that he has undergone an epileptic fit. The watchman placed his ears upon Arman's chest, he could hear a heartbeat, so, he rushed to get some water, splashing it on Arman's face until he gained consciousness after a while.

Arman opened his eyes and saw the watchman sitting beside him and the letter which was still in his hand. He reflected on the intense love Margaret held for him in the past, this thought made him impatient and restless and he screamed, "How far has today changed from yesterday!" Arman started crying, seeing him in this state, the watchman also started crying. Then the watchman hugged Arman to give him reassurance until he felt a little bit better. Arman requested the watchman to call a Hackney carriage for him, when it arrived Arman stood up with support from the watchman until he reached the carriage. Arman ordered the driver towards the Toren Hotel.

He had almost reached Toren Hotel when a beautiful carriage passed by like a thundering lightning with a man and woman in it. Arman did not recognize any of them at his first sight then realised it was John Phillip and Margaret. He reached the hotel and met his father in a worried and sad state. His father said to him, "What has happened to you O my son?"

He replied, "O my father Indeed she has deceived me!"

His father said, "This is what I used to warn you of O my son."

The day passed and the night fell. Arman spent the whole night in his bedroom awake. He thought about the chapter of his life which he had spent with Margaret. He pondered over all her behaviours until none of her love or sincerity remained rather he could only see her evil, wicked, deceptive and abhorrent behaviour from today. Her betrayal overshadowed everything. His mind went back to the final night he had seen her…

He remembered not seeing her not waiting at the balcony for him as she usually did when he returned after meeting his father. He recalled her hiding the letter of John Phillip which was in her hand when he had entered the room. She was clinging on to the letter very tightly whereas she had never done this before. He remembered her refraining engaging in conversation with him after he had narrated to her of the incident with his father. She was pretending that she was ill and upset and could not live without him. He remembered her insisting the next morning that he return to his father and beg him for mercy and love.

From all of this he concluded that when she had planned that when she had no money remaining, and his father would not provide provision, she would despise living with him and would think of a way to get rid of him. She waited until the letter of John Phillip's arrived and through it she finally found a way to free herself.

He remained upset and distressed until fatigue overtook his eyes and he fell asleep for a little while. When he awoke in the morning he went to his father in his bedroom and said to him, "O father, I have one last wish from you and I intend nothing else in exchange I will always obey you and will always for eternity listen to your orders whether I like it or dislike it. So, father, will you grant me my last wish?"

His father replied, "What is it?"

He said, "I would like you to give me fifteen thousand francs."

He replied, "What are you going to do with this?"

Arman said, "I would like to keep this a secret to myself and do not want to disclose it to anyone, even you." After a moment of hesitation his father gave him a cheque for the amount of money he had requested. Arman took it and sent it to Margaret along with a long letter which concluded with these words,

'Verily I have realised that I was living with a disrepute prostitute who could not keep a promise neither did she have any sense of responsibility. Thus, I am sending the payment for all the nights which I have spent with you in the past.'

Then he came out to prepare for his journey. He spent a whole day out of the hotel. Then he returned to the hotel in the last portion of the day. There he found a letter with his name on it. He tore open its seal. He discovered that those pages which he had sent to Margaret had returned to him just the way he had sent them. There was not even a word written in response. He intended to return the letter to her one more time but his father prevented him doing so saying, "You have promised that you will not go against my decision so you must listen." Thus, he listened. Then both travelled together that night back to Nice.

Like this, God had decreed to separate these two loyal friends and two sincere lovers. That young man returned to his father's care and the young lady returned to her former life, the life which she had eliminated herself from and which she feared. Each one of them felt sorrow and remorse for their companion. Neither did the days, the months nor did the years lessen their sorrow and remorse for each other.

***

There are a lot of unfortunate people in the world. However, the most unfortunate one is that troublesome and patient individual who is forced through the circumstances of life to bury his sorrows and pains in the depth of his heart and leave them there. In front of people he appears with a happy, smiling face as if he is not holding upon his shoulders the burdens of grief and sorrow.

210

This was the state which Margaret was encompassed with after she had returned to her former life. She was living with the people with an appearance other than her real appearance and in the state of sadness which she felt in isolation. When she was with people, she spent time with them laughing, playing, in a happy state and spent time with them peacefully. She used to glimmer in the crowds and gatherings, and she used to fill the eyes and the ears of people with sweet melodies. However, when she was alone in her bedroom and in the seclusion of night, her eyes would recall those honourable moments which she had spent in the company of Arman. Then she would remember that she ran away from his hands like a captured bird that flies away from the hands of its pursuer.

Indeed, she ended up living with people whom she did not know. She never found the joy of love with them. She had no alternative but to seduce and show love to them. She beautified herself for them the way they had wanted and the way they had desired. She used to kiss the faces of those whom she did not like. She used to hug those people who she did not even want to look at. She drank alcohol with every alcoholic whereas alcohol used to burn her insides. She used to dance with every dancer despite dancing used to cause pain in her joints. She used to laugh the laughter of happiness with a crying heart. She used to sing happy songs with a dead heart.

Thus, she used to get awfully upset when she remembered the past days of her life that had been filled with bliss. She used to leave the way clear for her sighs and her tears, she used to sigh as loud as she could and shed tears as much as she could until she felt a little better. Then she used to stand up and go to her wardrobe and take out a picture and place it on her chest. Then she would take refuge on her bed. It was the picture of Arman.

She continued to endure this adversity of living this fallen life, despite not having the strength to endure it. She lost weight and her colour changed. The beauty of her smiles vanished. She kept busy with herself and did not give time to John Phillip. Due to this he became fed up with her and separated from her and replaced her with another woman. After John Phillip, Margaret's other friends and associates started coming to her but not even one of them stayed other than recognising her symptoms and then leaving her. Hence, in the market of beauty her merchandise and stock had lost value. Now those individuals started desiring her, those who in the past, could not even dream to obtain the dust of the ground she had walked on.

At this point she needed money greatly. So, she started selling the remaining of her diamonds and gems but even after this, her debt remained. She sought help from a lot of her past friends. But only a handful of friends had helped her and this did not benefit her at all. Summons and letters from the debtors had started arriving, demanding she clear the outstanding amount. The matter became so bad that she was unable to pay any further payments. Accordingly, they bankrupted her and took away her belongings, her treasures, the household furniture and her clothes. Their conduct was extremely cold and merciless which increased her grief and her illness. Also, the remaining hope that she had left of life and its happiness came to an end. Thus, she forgot the whole world, its good and its bad, its life, its fortunes and its misfortunes. However, there was only one thought which went through her mind night and day. This was the wish to see Arman one last time before she died and met her Lord.

She had never written Arman a single word ever since She had parted from him. Neither did he write to her. In a distressed state, she went to her desk and penned the following;

'**Come to me O Arman, whether you are pleased or whether you are upset. I am ill and close to death. I would like to see you before I die and disclose to you the reason for my betrayal. Betrayal which hurt you immensely and still hurts to this day. I hope that you can forgive me in my last moments of my life. Then your pardoning and you being pleased with me becomes the complete lot of provisions which I will take with me to my grave. Remember O Arman, the first sentiment which joined us together, and because of it love was born in our hearts. That was an act of mercy and kindness. So, here is the poor, ill, young woman whom you showed mercy and kindness in the**

**days gone by when you loved her. Today she is calling
you to show mercy and kindness to her even though
you have forgotten her.**

**Regarding the letter which you wrote to me before
your journey, indeed I have forgiven everything your
said, even your statement that verily I was insincere in
my love, that I had greed for your money. This is
because, certainly I know that a woman who has been
lying all her life to men in terms of declaring her love,
will not find anyone who would believe her when she
tells the truth. Whatever has been done, the justice is
with God.'**

Then she waited for his coming for a very long time.
Thus, he never came, this increased her pain and sadness.
She started thinking badly of him. A thought had
appeared in her heart that verily he has forgotten her and
has discarded her from his memories. She presumed that
he did not care about her and he was not bothered with her
life or either with her death. She speculated that he was
not concerned about her wellbeing.

This presumption, however, was untrue. This was
because Arman was never informed of the letter which
she had sent him. Although he travelled to Nice he did
not have power to stay there except for a few days. This
was because he started becoming restless and his heart
became constrained, failing to obtain any peace. Thus, he
sought permission from his father to travel towards some

western countries to please his heart and to lessen his pain. His father gave him the permission, and then he travelled to Alexandria, Egypt. He stayed there for a few months. He wrote to his father from there a few times. Then he left Alexandria and started roaming to other towns. He never stayed in one town except that his restlessness took him to another town. Now he had stopped writing to his father and his father was unaware of his location.

Whenever Margaret had sent him her letter to Nice, Arman's father had read it and treasured it with him. His farther had no means of sending it to him. Margaret on the other hand, had no knowledge of this. Thus, Margaret became extremely sad over her failing hope.

Eventually, despair had penetrated her heart like the shadow of death. Now, she knew that she would leave this world deprived of everything, her condition deteriorated further and she took refuge towards silence. Whenever her doctor came, when she was in severe pain, she never complained of her pain to the doctor. She used to hear the noise of the debtors and their pleas in the courtyard of her house. She never asked them what they wanted.

However, when she felt a little bit better in terms of having relief from her pain, she embarking on a hackney carriage, travelled to Bougival, visiting the house where she had been living in happiness. The house was still maintained well. She passed by its rooms and its courtyards. She would sit in every place Arman had sat. She would look through all those windows which Arman used to look out of with her. She would kiss every sign and remaining mark affiliated with Arman. She would kiss the glass which Arman used to drink from. She kissed the flower which he used to like. She kissed the pen which he used to write with. She kissed the book which he used to read from. When she felt tired, she would sit down and take a rest. Whenever her thoughts hovered towards old times, her imagination used to make her believe that Arman was sitting in front of her and telling her his childhood stories in Nice, or that he was disclosing his love to her from the depths of his heart. She would smile contemplating over these things. She used to feel such a joy in her heart, a joy which the pious would feel in the highest gardens of Paradise. Then she would open her eyes, only to discover the seclusion, the quietness and the loneliness. She would cry as much as God would allow her to do so.

Then she would return to her house in Paris where she would sit in her chair and would pretend Arman was there and would talk to him about all the things bothering her heart.

(The upcoming accounts of Diaries contribute towards the missing elements of this story. Through these accounts the readers can understand the reasons why Margaret had left Arman. Hence, the following accounts of the diaries are a part of this story.)

THE VICTIM

Margaret's Diary

Memories of Margaret
Accounts from Margaret's Diary

15th December 1850

Dear Arman:

You did not write to me nor did you come to see me, as if, you fear that I intend to return to our past life. How can I return that time? If you saw me now, you would see an upset woman who is leaving this world, incapable of doing anything. All I want from you is, is to see you at my bedside in the final moments of my life, so that I can apologise to you regarding the crime I committed against you, bid you farewell and go to my grave.

O Arman, I did not deceive you neither was I disloyal to you. Certainly, the letter you saw in my hand, was not the letter of Mr John Phillip the way you had assumed, but it was the letter of your father which I had received an hour before you arrived to Bougival. This is what the letter said;

Dear Madame,

I intend to meet you tomorrow in your house at ten o'clock in the morning regarding an exclusive matter between me and you. I do not want Arman present nor do I want him to have any knowledge of it. Adding to that, he must not know that I have sent this letter to you. Indeed, I do have a very good opinion about you which gives me hope that whatever I have asked you, will remain secret between us until we meet. Goodbye.

Duval

However, when I read the letter, I knew what he wanted from this meeting. I realised what was coming in this meeting. In fact, I had guessed the discussion that took place between you and him and that certainly you had rejected his proposal and he had fallen into despair. My heart urged me to decline this meeting and to disclose everything to you. Then I felt ashamed and embarrassed, that such an honourable man; the likes of your father was entrusting me with such a big secret that he does not deem me a fallen woman as he had presumed me to be. I hoped that in our meeting, I would obtain from him what he was hoping to obtain from me. So, I hid the matter of the letter from you. I hid all that which was in my heart from you. I was not lying regarding the illness and the pain which I was complaining about. The night which I spent in my bed after I had parted from you, was one of the most traumatic of my life.

I stayed in bed until morning broke, then I forced you to go and meet your father. I knew that when you go to him you will be unable to meet him. I also knew that if you were to meet him, the meeting will not give you any benefit. However, I feared that if your father came to visit and found you here with me he would see it as my breaching his trust!

Only a few moments after you left, your father arrived at Bougival as stated in his letter. He sought my permission to enter, as he entered I saw his eyes full of anger blazing like fire. However, I did not care and invited him to sit down. He did not. He did not greet me. The first thing with which he addressed me was, "What do you intend to do with my son O lady?" He was staring at me intently. I felt really disheartened and wanted to say to him,

"Sir, do you know that you are in my house, and I never invited you to come and see me, but it was you who invited yourself." Then I remembered his position as your father and did not respond.

He walked, hitting his stick and stamping his feet on the ground until he was near me and with a look of disgust uttered, "Verily my son has spent all the wealth which was in his hand upon you. There is no doubt that he had a lot of wealth in his hand. He spent all that wealth which I had sent him upon you as well, and indeed I have sent him wealth beyond my capacity. He does not have the power to give you more than that which he has given you.

Neither is it in my power to bring down from the heavens gold which could be rained over you.

So, leave him and let him be alone. The towns are filled with boys whom their parents do not need, Indeed I need my son because he is my only son. I have not been given sustenance for other than him. Whereas, a lady who possesses the wealth of beauty like you, can never be disadvantaged in life. All her requirements and the necessities of life can be fulfilled."

Thus, his words penetrated in my heart the way fever penetrates to the bones. I felt that certainly this statue which is in front of me is not talking to me but is poisoning me severely with his words. I felt a sense of inferiority which I had never felt ever! However, despite this, I remained calm, remaining patient and controlling myself and in a very low, steady voice which contained neither any anger nor any indications of being upset, I replied,

"O sir, yes without a shadow of doubt I do love your son, but I am not greedy over his money, however, if I was greedy for his money, then certainly I would have parted from him three months ago, this was when all the money that he had finished. Nay, but I would have left him before this. This is because the elite and the wealthy people from amongst this town were bargaining a price in concerns of me even till today. These people were more in wealth than Arman and live life to the maximum. Adding to that, indeed your son has not spent on me that wealth which you are talking about other than only a little, most has been spent on himself. Despite that, I had the power to reject and refuse that small amount even if I wanted to but I did not want him to doubt me or feel any pain. That is why I used to accept his small and meagre gifts which he would give me from time to time. If, what you say is correct, that whatever was in his hand had transferred into my hands then unquestionably I would have become extremely rich. I have never struggled neither have I endured the problems and adversities which I am bearing and enduring today. Had you had queried about me, you would have come to realize that I am a poor woman in strained circumstances. I am not the owner of any worldly assets other than my jewellery, my carriage and the furniture of my house, if only these had remained mine, most of these things have become the property of the usurers and the loan sharks. I do not know what is coming towards my direction tomorrow. Adding to that, if you do want to know then let me inform you of the thing which I have hid from all people including your son."

Then I went to my drawer where I kept my official documentation. Thus, from there I brought the receipts and the documents which were inclusive upon the sale of my jewellery, my horses and the furniture of my house. In addition to that, I had even brought the deeds of those things which through pawning I had taken out on mortgage.

Duval continued turning over the pages for a while, and contemplated upon the dates for a long time. Then he folded up the documents and returned them to me. He put his head down and remained silent, not saying a word. He took the chair in front of him and dragging it sat down resting his head upon his stick. By this point, his anger had cooled down. The black cloud which was shadowing his face before had disappeared. I continued with my conversation;

"Other than that, O sir, verily I am not complaining nor am I seeking revenge from you. Indeed, I have lived days entailing extreme hardships and difficulties which have killed all my desires for life in my heart. These calamities have caused me to forget the colours of life along with its pride. Thus, I have become a woman who does not care of what the future will bring. Being wealthy or being poor, both are equal to me. Whether I wear jewellery and be scented with fragrance, whether I live in a castle or whether I live in a cottage I do not care. I am not bothered anymore if I ride on a carriage or walk upon my feet. However, all that I request from my life, from God and from you is that, I would like to have Arman, so that he can share with me the pains and sorrows of life. Having him will then help me to overcome the troubles and problems of life until God decrees for me a verdict the way He chooses. If, however, life is extended for me, then I would spend it thanking you and praising you, showing sincerity to you in secrecy and in the open. Alternatively, if I was to die, then the last words which I shall utter, would be the supplication to God, begging and crying to Him to bless you and your family abundantly and that He bestows over you a beautiful veil in your present and in your future."

I inclined in front of him and held the cloth from the corner of his clothes. Thus, at this point I lost control of withholding my tears and said,

"O master, have mercy on me. Verily I am a troubled, poor woman. Certainly, the necessities of life had forced me in the beginning of my life to stand upon the edge of a ditch, that ditch whose corner a prostitute stands. Thus, I fell into that ditch unwillingly and hatefully. The life which destiny had ordained for me to live in, I had accepted. Nevertheless, I struggled to live like this. I became a woman standing in two ways. Nor was I chaste so that I could be blessed with living a life like honourable women. Neither did my heart die which prevented me to live like a characterless and fallen women. In your son, I found an individual who loved me sincerely solely for myself. He cherished me with his love and with his sincerity which no one from the mankind had ever done before. Thus, I fell in love with him causing me to forget my falling down and my prostitution related affairs. Accordingly, I started loving life, which I had hated and felt disgusted over before. Now I have begun living my life with sincerity. O master do not deprive me of this gem. O master do not cause a separation between me and him. If, however you were still to do this, then you will make me a very unfortunate and an extremely distressed woman. You will fill my life with grief and sorrows. Whereas I see and consider you beyond and above one who builds their foundations of happiness and comfort upon the misfortunes of a poor woman the likes of myself.

What is going to be my outcome tomorrow if I were to become alone, boycotted from this world, and not find for myself a friend nor a helper? Am I going to return to my former life, the life which I hated and the life which I am frightened of? In that case, I would be returning to my sins and my crimes. Alternatively, I could commit suicide to escape the tortures and the ordeals of life. I do not have the power to carry out either of these actions. Therefore, please advance forth your beautiful hand and save me from this deep ditch which no one has the power to save me other than yourself.

I know that certainly you need your son, and without question you have more right over him from the entire creation from the earth. However, I do know that indeed you are extremely kind and merciful. Verily in these blessed moments, you are not going to refuse being charitable to an ill, troubled lady, like myself who's illness has worn her out. O honourable gentleman, I do not ask you for money, neither a connection nor any utilities of life, but I ask you to allow Arman to remain with me. This is because his staying with me would be the salvation for my life and for my fortune. Please be charitable to me, verily you are amongst the good doers."

After I had said all this, I felt and sensed that he was moving on his chair. He raised his head and looked at me with a glance which was less in anger and rage than his first sight and said, "And how are you both going to live?"

I replied, "I have remaining with me my gems and my jewellery which soon I shall sell and then with its money, I will live in some corner from the corners of Paris with Arman as poor straitened people. No one will see us nor sense our existence. It will be sufficient for us - our blessing of love which will replace all other blessings and happiness of the world."

Duval said, "In fact this is the misfortune itself. This is because love is like vegetation; a plant which requires shade, otherwise the hot sun of misfortune would exterminate it. In respect to all the blessings contained within this world which have not been obtained through money nor without any asset are inevitably false. These are nothing but the illusions of the mind which have no place.

Today, both of you are happy and prosperous because in your hands you have money from which you can live with. Also, it is because of this money, you both are living in this beautiful house which is located on top of this high mountain besides this astonishing lake. The instance your hands will be deprived from this money and from this blessing, both of you will become troubled and then your states will automatically deprive you from love and its pleasures. At that point, both of you will become burdened and tired. Most likely that feeling which both of you will feel of being burdened at that time will inevitably take you towards the opposite spectrum of love.

Without doubt, love entails an art of madness, and the craziest ideology is that love makes two lovers believe that their love will remain forever and that the days of catastrophes will not change their love. They believe that the interchanging and alternating days will not affect their love at all. However, when both lovers come back to their senses, they realize that certainly love is a colour from the colours of the heart. It is desire and longing which brings love and it is something else which takes it away. Certainly, hunger and straitened circumstances exterminate love. This is especially when hunger increases and its knots become tighter. Without a doubt, a person requires to live and to maintain his life before he could desire love, its pleasures and satisfy its yeaning.

Indeed, I know my son's circumstances which you do not know O lady. I know without question, he does not have the power to live this poor life the way you are expecting him to do. Now he has become a poor young man who is not the owner of anything in this world except for a small piece of land which he has inherited from his mother. This small piece of land however will not enrich him neither it would enrich you. I am not a person with a lot of money from which I have the power to protect and provide for him living this long life in Paris anymore the way he has been living here. Therefore, there remains for him no other option except to live of your money. This however, is a thing which I am not pleased with neither would Arman be pleased with. O my lady, excuse me for saying this to you, certainly all the problems and the worries of life, I and Arman can bear, other than to listen to the people saying, 'Indeed Arman Duval's girlfriend has sold all her diamonds and her jewellery which were gifted to her from her previous lovers so that she can spend that money on Arman.'

O my daughter, please forgive me for my conduct and pardon my harshness and my anger. This is because it is extremely difficult for an old father, the likes of me, to see his only son whom he had expected to fulfil all the hopes of his household; to fall in this deep ditch which has no end to it. Hence, his father's heart would therefore only inflame with fear and sorrow.

Certainly, ever since Arman got to know you, he has forgotten me and has forgotten his sister. Neither has he remembered me nor has he remembered her. Verily his sister has been critically ill for the past few months. I had written to Arman telling him to come so that he could help and assist me, but he never came nor did he reply to my letter. I was in a state that if I had died, I would have not seen him. At that point I would have been taking remorse and sorrow to my grave which no one had ever taken with them before.

O respectable lady, you are true in what you said that, Arman did not spend all that wealth which he had in his hand on you. This is because only yesterday I found out that he has been gambling for quite some time and he has lost a lot of money through gambling. I am aware that you do not know anything about this. Thus, my heart will not be at peace if I were to leave him in this town. This is because then he will indulge himself in this new problematic way of life completely where he has already stepped in to. In this path at some point, he will be afflicted with some big loss. It may at that point become crucial for me to hold his hand in that situation and give him all my life earnings which I have reserved for my old age and for the wedding arrangements for my daughter. Thus, all three of us, me, Arman and my daughter will then die on one day.

O my daughter, what would be your outcome if after staying with you for a long time, Arman becomes disheartened from you and his sight hovers upon another woman other than you? At that point your pain and grief of tomorrow would be more severe and greater than of today. What would be your state when you will become completely tight upon your money one day belonging to your frightful and lonely days of life? Then by all means, you would prefer returning to your former life which encompasses a delight, a gathering, some noise and the spotlight. You must not forget that Arman is a young ardent and a pessimistic man. If you were to go back to your first life, then Arman would reject you because of this. It may be that he might retaliate with his rivalry because of you. Through this, troubles will descend upon him. Hence, from his opposition he might get hurt and may forfeit his life in the process and at that point you will be responsible for giving me pain.

O my dear, what would be your answer tomorrow if Arman gets struck by an arrow from the decree of destiny in front of this poor crying father and that when his father comes to you and demands from you the blood retribution for his son? Adding to that what would be the state of your pain and grief in front of a crying and a troublesome father?"

Then after this, your father started shaking and his eyes started rolling in distress, as if he was watching the account which he had just narrated right before his eyes. Then he went quiet for a while and then he looked at me with a look which contained softness and was full of love and kindness. Then he started speaking,

"O Margaret, you have ranked higher in my eyes than I had expected. You are an honourable soul from amongst women. Verily, I have found in you such qualities and such attributes that I have not found but only in a few men before. Also, I have rarely seen this honour in women. If, however, honour was to be divided between mankind per their dignity and their attributes, then certainly your portion from it would be greater and most substantial.

O Margaret until I am alive, I will never forget your favour that you did upon me in terms of hiding the affair of that letter which I had sent to you, and that you safeguarded its secret at a time when most people would have revealed it. I will not forget your patience and you lowering your gaze in front of me despite having the power to say and do as you pleased to me in your house. You remained quiet in front of me during my harshness, my anger and my insane behaviour. Also, I will never forget what you spent on my son from your heart and from your wealth, despite him not knowing where you were spending it from. You did this only because of loyalty and to maintain his self-respect and honour.

Without question, the sacrifice which you made for my son yesterday was very big. However, today I have come to beg you for another sacrifice, which is a greater sacrifice then yesterdays. This sacrifice is for my daughter. There is no ground upon which I can intercede to you to fulfil my request other than expecting you to listen to me through your kind and noble heart.

Indeed, I have left Susan, Arman's sister behind who is struggling in her bed with her illness. She was enduring more pain than she could bear and is extremely weak in body. This is because her fiancé who she loved to bits left her two months ago, he has not come to visit her nor has she seen him. Indeed, I was unaware of the reason to her illness before this day, as I was only speculating and assuming its causes until I stayed awake sitting at her bedside one night. When I did this, I discovered that her feverish symptoms had reached their peak and that she had reached such a point that now she was talking gibberish and nonsense. I heard her saying aloud the name of her fiancé many times. She cried every time she uttered his name. That is when I realized what the cause of her illness was. Upon the second day, I went to the father of her fiancé to ask him what thing had created doubt for his son regarding my daughter and the reason for him not meeting his daughter anymore. His father mentioned a reason to me which had some of your affairs included within it O respectable lady. Do you permit me to narrate to you his reason?"

My heart trembled severely and I felt that bad was drawing near to me slowly but surely. However, I kept calm and said to him, "Yes I grant you permission O sir."

He said, "Verily her fiancé's father answered my question by saying, 'Indeed my family is a very honourable and a well dignified family who do not tie the bond of matrimony with another family except if it is likewise a noble and a well-respected family from all angles. Certainly, it has come to my attention the despicable low lifestyle of your son and how he lives in Paris. Without question, your son has been living with a very well-known and a very notorious prostitute for a very long time. People are testifying to this cursed lifestyle that he is living with a woman who has been used and abused. My heart will never allow such a person like your son who has a bad character, living an immoral and roguish lifestyle, to become the brother in-law for my son. Adding to that, I do not want to bring shame upon my daughter in respect of this.' Then her fiancé's father stopped. I endured his hard, sharp words with patience and tolerance. This is because I was fearful for my daughter.

I then said to him, 'Are you true in what you are saying?' He presented to me such evidence that I realized what he was saying was true. I did not see any other alternative but to accept whatever he was saying. I then requested him not to make any prompt decisions regarding the marriage until I go to Paris and return from there. This is what I am burdened with and that is why I have come to Paris. This is my story which I have come to narrate to you. I await your decision regarding this matter. Indeed, I have hidden the matter of our meeting from all mankind including my son Arman. Therefore, please contemplate over this matter and tell me what your decision is?"

Then he lowered his head for quite some time. When he raised his head, he had tears filling his eyes. When he commenced his discussion, he did not have the ability to talk. Thus, I felt sorry for the state he was in and I considered his calamity big, which led me to forget my calamity irrespective of his. Silence stretched between as I did not know what to say to him. There came a point where his distressed state calmed. He took my hand and held it between his arms. Returning to his conversation he began saying,

"O Margaret, certainly the life of my daughter is in front of you.   Please Margaret save me from this trial. Margaret, bestow upon me a favour which I will never forget till death.   Indeed, I do not have the power to see her dying in front of me. If, however she was to die then certainly I would also die with her grief, pain and sadness. In one day, both of us would be put into one grave. Indeed, I am still grieving the death of her mother for five years, the symptoms of which are still upon my heart even today.   Now I do not have the power to witness this incident regarding my daughter.   Indeed, I love my daughter dearly, I do not have the power to see her enduring distress and calamity at any time, so how am I going to see her enduring the pains of death?

O Margaret, indeed you do not know my daughter. Hand on heart, I am certain that if you were to see her, you also would love her the way I love her and you would also be merciful to her the way I show her mercy and you too would sacrifice for her whatever is in your power showing kindness and mercy to her.

Verily she is extremely beautiful and her fairness is like that of a star. She is pure like the purity of an Angel and her innocence is like the innocence of a child. Thus, for her soft and tender life please show kindness to her so that happiness remains for her.   This is because she is not deserving of a misfortune.   Indeed, today she is living upon a hope which I have entrusted in her heart the day I embarked my journey. If now I return to her with failure,

I would be returning to her like a despaired murderer descending upon her death.

O Margaret, certainly you do love Arman and certainly I truly believe that you are completely devoted in his love sincerely. Therefore, preform an act which only devoted lovers can perform. Sacrifice your love for him and for his future. If, however you cannot do this for him, then do it for me.

Verily it is you who has said to me that certainly Arman is the only individual who has loved you sincerely for yourself, more than he has loved you for himself. Give him expiation for this love. In fact, give him a better requital then he has given to you in this love and let your comfort and satisfaction become a virtue which you will obtain after parting from him through pain and adversities, knowing that certainly he has become prosperous after you, knowing that indeed you have saved a young poor girl from the hands of death and knowing that you have saved an extremely old man from grief."

It was at this point when his voice shook as he sobbed and fell on his chair in front of me and said in a dying person's voice,

"O Margaret, show me mercy! O Margaret, show kindness upon my weakness and upon my old age. O Margaret, please bestow upon me the future of my son and the life of my daughter."

Then after this, he did not have the power to speak another word. He put his head down upon the chair where he was sitting and burst out crying.

O Arman, only if you had seen me in this situation, and only if you had seen the pain and the agony which I was enduring, and only if you had seen my tears which were flowing upon my cheeks feeling sorry for your father. Verily he was talking but my tears were flowing with each word.

Verily the most supreme and prestigious person is whom who is great in everything including being big in his sorrows and in his hardships. Indeed, I thought to myself when your father was crying and beseeching in front of me, that verily every tear from his tears will descend the wrath of God upon the earth, and that every sigh from amongst his sighs will burn the horizon and the atmosphere of the sky.

Verily I felt extremely guilty over this matter in my heart that such an old, pure, respectable man was kneeling in front of a fallen woman like myself. I felt such shame that I wished that the earth would tear open under my feet and I could bury myself in there eternally.

I started pondering over his problem, about his story which he had narrated to me and regarding the predicament he was in. Thus, I concluded that verily I am the one responsible for giving misfortunes to this respectable and honourable family, to this father, to his son and to his daughter. I found this thought very heavy upon my chest and upon my conscience. This situation became loathsome for me. I thought to myself that if my spirit had appeared in front of me verily I would throw it down from such a height that no place after this would combine my body and soul together. I thought to myself that verily my past life which I spent in crimes and in sins has indeed cut off from me the path of modesty and chastity. Now I do not even have the right to desire the life of chastity nor do I have the right to even quarrel with life for its fortunes and its happiness. Certainly, the crime which I have committed myself in the past verily I had committed on my own accord myself. Thus, it is only right now that only I bear its burden lest that I put it on anyone else's shoulder besides me. If it is destined for me to die a death of an inferior woman, then that is inevitable because I am a fallen woman. If it is decreed for my future to entail misfortunes and hardships, then that is also inevitable. This is certainly because the future is the outcome and the result of the past and encountering this outcome is inevitable.

O Arman, at this point I remembered you a lot. I thought to myself how am I going to separate from you and how am I going to have the power to live without you. I gathered that it will be me who is going to end my life with my own hands. This was because there was no other way of pleasing your father nor was there a way to give him his ultimate satisfaction other than to break ties with you, showing resentment towards you and appearing in front of you as a cheating and disloyal woman. I was forced to connect with someone else other than you to make sure that you see me and that you hear me. I did this only for you to leave me the way a despaired person would, in such a state that you are unaware that your father had any share in this whatsoever. Thus, in one split second, I made a firm decision to part from you and portray resentment towards you. I knew that when I left you, it would be inevitable for me to return to my former life, the life which I hated and disliked. This was because till this day, Duke Mohan had not forgiven or forgotten my betrayal towards him. So how can I go back to him? My former life was inevitable because I needed sustenance in life from which I could treat my illness and pay for my debts. For one hour, these thoughts circulated my head. Then, these thoughts prolonged until it was near that I go against my decision as then I casted my sight upon your father's face drenched in tears. At once, I became strong and collected myself, I went towards him leaving everything behind me.

O Arman to leave you was extremely difficult for me. However, to see your father crying in front of me was more difficult. It was difficult for me to endure that I was going to become the reason for the death of your sister and for her loss.

Without question O Arman I love you. I recognize the pain of love and its heat which generates in hearts. Indeed, when your father was talking to me about your sister and about her devastation, I was picturing her lying down on her bed. I was seeing her hands pleading with me, crying and beseeching me saying, 'Save me O lady, have mercy upon my weakness and upon my youth.' I felt her words penetrating my heart in a way that only one in a similar situation could feel.

Indeed, I was deprived from the virtue of marriage and its happiness in the beginning of my life which caused great calamities to befall me that make me cry even today. Thus, my pain does not increase nor reignite except when a woman in similar circumstances is in hardship.

This is because verily I am in love and likewise she is also in love. Therefore, it is inevitable for one of us to sacrifice our love for the other. Thus, I give preference to sacrifice my love for her, only because she is your sister and only because she has not sinned in her life nor is she entitled for this misfortune.

Whenever I imagined that indeed soon your sister will become prosperous and content after me, and that she will appear in front of me wearing a white beautiful wedding dress and walking to the church having her fiancé besides her, my heart became filled with joy and happiness.

Yes, certainly this strike is extremely painful and I shall feel it in the future. My heart will not be able to endure this pain. However, I will try my utmost best to endure this pain through patience and serenity. This is because your father will soon become pleased with me and soon you will come to know and learn about the secret of my sacrifice. Then you will love me more than you had loved me ever before. Indeed, at that point, your sister will also become happy and will be indulged in a prosperous life. Perhaps my name might be included amongst those names which your sister will supplicate for in her prayers beseeching for mercy and for gratification.

Nevertheless, the time came where I could say my last words to your father. Verily it was a very distressing moment for me. I asked God to forgive me for my past and future sins. I supplicated to God that He never allows another woman taste the bitterness of this pain and torture after me.

I hauled myself off the chair and dragged my feet towards your father like a dead person walks towards their grave. I knelt in front of him and took hold of his hand, he looked at me restlessly so, I said to him, "O my respected sir, do you believe that I love your son?"

He replied, "Yes."

I said, "I love him with an ardent love with all my being, do you believe that?"

He again replied, "Yes."

I then said, "Certainly this was the love which completed all my hopes and all my fortunes. It was the only thing I possessed in this world, do you acknowledge this too?"

Again, he replied, "Yes my daughter."

I then said, "Indeed because of your daughter I have sacrificed my love. Return to her and give her the good news of her bright future and tell her that, indeed there is a woman who does not know you, neither has she ever seen you, but she loves you and is very kind to you. She will die very soon because of you. Beg God to shower His mercy and forgiveness over her."

His face glittered up with joy and happiness. He left no word of praise neither a word of gratitude, except that he showered them upon me. His happiness and his joy made me forget the severe pain and trauma which engulfed my heart. My pain and my sorrows changed into peace and harmony at that time. I praised God for this, as your father did not see anything upon my face which would lessen his excitement and his happiness.

At that point I felt some movement next to the door of the room, when I looked I saw my maid Prudence who was gesturing at me with her hand. I went to her and then she gave me a letter which the postman had delivered. I read the address only to learn that it was a letter from Mr John Phillip therefore, I already knew what the letter contained before I had read it. It occurred to me that God had sent this as a sign for me. I went running to my desk and read the letter. Then I wrote a reply in the following words, 'Indeed, soon I will be having the evening dinner with you.' Then I gave that piece of paper to Prudence for her to put into the post box.

I then returned to your father and said to him, "Indeed Arman does not know anything about this meeting of yours with me. So, do not tell him about it when you meet him. I shall write to him soon, telling him of our separation. In this letter, he will not doubt anyone except me, he will know that certainly you were not involved in what happened. Arman will come to know today or tomorrow that verily I have joined connections with another man other than him and have broken my promise with him. Then he will inevitably find no other alternative but to travel back with you breaking all hopes and ties with me. This tragedy will cause him distress for a couple of weeks. Then after that he will not care about this anymore. My love in his heart will deteriorate, besides this, I only have one request from you, will you bestow this upon me?"

He replied, "Yes, I will bestow upon you anything you want."

I said, "Indeed I am an ill woman who is close to her death. Certainly, the illness which has afflicted me, a lot of people talk about it that verily it does not detach from a person, whether that illness is prolonged or whether it is short until it takes that person to his or her grave. All that I ask from you is that, on the day when you find out that indeed I have reached my deathbed, you grant Arman permission to come to see me so that I could see him, give him my last farewells and apologize to him regarding my betrayal because of you. This is because I am not going to bear loss in his love and in his dignity whether I am alive or whether I am dead."

He looked at me with the eyes which were drenched in tears and said, "O my daughter, may the Lord shower his mercy upon you, indeed I promise you whatever you want and I will pray to God to grant you forgiveness and patience." Then after that he intended to give me something as a help, thus I strongly refused it and said to him, "O my respected gentleman, I have not sold myself, I have gifted myself." Accordingly, he took hold of my head in his hands and kissed me on my forehead. This kiss was an excellent compensation for the sacrifice which I had given. Then he said his farewells to me and departed.

After this, I stood up and went towards my wardrobe. I gathered my clothes and what was remaining from my jewellery. I travelled with my maid Prudence to Paris. I went to my house. It is then I wrote to you the letter which you received. Only God knows how many tears I shed and only He knows how many times my heart stopped upon each word and what I went through. I gave that letter to the watchman of the house, entrusting him to give it to you upon your arrival. I went to Mr John Phillip to fulfil the promise of dinner.

Indeed, in terms of my life with that man, I do not have the power to narrate to you anything from his affair other than just to say to you, that indeed, he did not find in me the woman he was expecting nor did he find a woman of his desires. Neither did I see in him a man who could love me and mix in with me. Thus, we stayed separate. I became a woman who had lost the ability to distinguish an honest person from a liar.

This is my story O Arman the way it went and this is the betrayal which I committed with you. So, do you still consider me to be a cheat and a fraud after this?

My heart desires that verily I die before I could see you. I believe that whatever is in your heart of animosity and hatred towards me will perish after I die. Certainly, you will return to Paris the moment someone will inform you of my death for you to visit the grave of the woman who was the joy of your heart and belonged to the best days of your life. She will leave this world empty handed of everything, including your love and kindness. However, whenever you become curious about what happened to her after you left and that what led her to her death, you are welcome to find out.

Therefore, I am writing everything in my diary which I am going to leave with Prudence, hoping that perhaps you will read it someday in the future. Then you will look at these pages as you would look at a holy book, which will verify all that I went through and you will forgive me.

Thus, your forgiveness and your pardoning will then enlighten the darkness in my grave and the fear clutching my soul will vanish.

***

3rd January 1851

O my Arman where are you? You have gone far away from me. Indeed, your body and your soul both, have become distant from me. This is because you have not replied to my letter which I wrote to you, in which, I invited you to come to see me in order to hear my last confession. I believe you have not come because the anger and hostility that you hold in your heart towards me has led you to forget and neglect me. You have become a person who does not remember me like a lover remembers his beloved. Neither are you showing kindness to me the way a friend shows mercy to a friend. Whatever God intends let it be, and may that blessing always stay with you and your family and your people. Indeed, I am not hostile against you, neither am I wanting any revenge from you. I do not hold anything other than love in my heart and sincerity for you. I am pleased with everything which you came with and whatever you have left.

A few days have passed and I have not seen anyone from amongst the people. This is because my doctor has prevented me from going out. Also, indeed my friends who know me from the past have verily sufficed upon sending me 'get well' cards only thorough my maid instead of coming themselves to see me. After they drop off their cards, they run away like people who are afraid of something. Certainly, they are the same people who before today, would wait hours on end to deliver cards in person to me, waiting for hours until I used to grant them the permission for a meeting. However, when they were granted the permission of a meeting they would rush inside with happiness. If, however, they were deprived from the meeting, they used to go back upset.

I do not understand; why do not they stop giving the greeting cards the way they have stopped meeting me? Indeed, they are hoping to see me in between them soon. They are hoping that I will start living with them and mixing in with them the way they used to live with me in the past. However, they are wrong.

Whatever they have done, they have done good. However now, I can only feel content and at ease through myself and not through anyone else. The only reason I feel content with myself is because when I am alone I have the power to ask my heart about you. Thus, my heart reminds me about you and about those days of happiness which I had spent with you at Bougival. I remember those days as this is all I have left of you.

O Arman, I never thought that a human body could endure the tragedies which I am enduring. Indeed, moments have passed which I truly believed was the pain and struggles of the soul at the time of death and verily these are the last moments of my life. Whenever I do come out of that state, I ask myself, if I cannot bear this pain of illness, how am I possibly going to bear the pain of death?

Has destiny written that I will see you besides me in my lifetime? Only if my heart can convince me of this. Then that would inevitably cure my illness and my soul will return, restoring my peace and my happiness. Is God going to decree this for me?

I do not know. Thus, the future is in the hands of God. He decrees whatever He wants and He does whatever He pleases.

*****

24th January 1851

I did not part from my bed for many days until today. I sat down at the window for a little while looking out to observe ordinary life. My sight landed upon many people whom I recognised. They were walking very happily on their ways. Nevertheless, I did not see anyone from amongst them who looked up even once at my window. It was, as if, they were walking past a house which they did not recognize and that they had no connection with ever before.

How unfortunate is my loneliness? How tight has my chest become? How heavy has this wall become which surrounds me?

I do not have the power to look at my bed because my heart is telling me that soon my bed will become the ladder to my grave. Neither can I stand in front of my mirror because the mirror tells me the worst things and bad omens about me. Nor do I have the power to look out of my window because this reminds me of my past blissful life which has become forbidden for me. So now where shall I go? And how shall I live?

I do not eat but one type of food. I do not see but only the same scene every day. I do not hear but only the voice of my doctor and the voice of my maid whenever they enquire about me, every morning and every evening. I give them one reply every time. This has continued as now I have become tired and fallen into despair. I feel as if my heart is imprisoned in my chest and that my body is imprisoned in my room. Sometimes I encounter such moments that my mind stops working and my heart stops beating. I feel that I have become cut off from yesterday, today and tomorrow, in fact from everything in my life as now I am standing alone.

The severe coughing has shackled the insides of my chest. Only sometimes my eyes catch sleep. The doctor continues to punish me severely through his injections and his medication. Every day I am feeling that my heart is becoming tighter and my eyes have increased in darkness. I feel that my life is slowly but surely going far away from me. Now I presume that I have become a distant shadow. So, when is my torture going to finish?

***

30th January 1851

Today I heard some noise in the courtyard. I enquired from Prudence about it. Thus, she went, then she came back informing me, "O my beloved lady, verily the bailiffs are seizing the furniture of our house."

Thus, I replied, "Leave them, let them do whatever they want to do." Not even a little while had passed by that the legal officers entered my room creating havoc. Not even one of them bothered to take off their hat for the lady of the house out of respect. Neither did anyone lower their voice to show kindness to a troubled ill lady. They started walking and registering an account of everything which their sight had landed upon. I became frightened lest that they make a note in their register about my diary. Accordingly, I gestured and gave a sign to Prudence to go and hide it away from them and she did. I thanked God for this.

They advanced forth towards my bed. Then one of the debtors requested that the bed should also be seized saying that it is very expensive. Then he said, "Soon on the day of the auction, this bed would prove highly beneficial." The evictor explained to the debtor that certainly the law does not permit this, and exempts beds and carpets from being seized. The bailiff drew near to the debtor and whispered in his ear. I am guessing that he said this, "Indeed you will have the power to do this after her death." They departed after leaving a guard standing at the doorstep of my house. The guard never left his place, guarding my house day and night.

I wrote a letter to Duke Mohan. This was the first time I had written to him since I had left him. I wrote to him asking him for forgiveness for my sin which I had committed with him. I then complained to him about all the calamities which the hands of destiny had given to me. I gave him an oath and the medium of the remembrance of his respected daughter, begging him to come to me and to meet me. Thus, he did this and came. The moment he was next to me, he saw me and started crying. I did not know whether he was crying over me, or whether he was observing my circumstances which then made him remember the circumstances of his daughter in the last moments of her life, which then led him to cry. Then Duke Mohan remained with me for a while, standing head bowed in silence. He did not talk to me but only a little. He did not mention even a word of what had taken place in the past. Then he went and left in the hands of Prudence a bundle of money which Prudence spent on buying some provisions and sustenance. In addition to that, with the aid of that money Prudence delayed the eviction of household furniture for a couple of months.

I do not have the power to write to you more than that which I have written. This is because certainly the doctor is constantly taking blood from my body. This has weakened my body. Thus, now I do not feel anything other than devastating pain.

***

2nd February 1851

Certainly, this day was the happiest and the most soothing day from my days. This is because indeed today, a letter from your father arrived which stated;

O my Dear,

Indeed, I am enormously upset and extremely distressed for you. Indeed, I found out yesterday through some people who came to Nice, that you have been extremely ill for two months. It has also been brought to my attention that you hardly come out of your house. I pray to God that He grants you recovery and patience. I will beg Him to recompense you with the best reward for the pain and calamities which you have endured because of me and my daughter. Also, let me give you the glad tiding that indeed God has accepted your sacrifice which you sent forth for my daughter. Verily Susan got married to her fiancé twenty days ago, and she is content with her life. Even though she does not know about our secret, I have still told her as I did not mention your name, that certainly there are some people that have sacrificed their life and happiness for you to prosper. Therefore, do not

ever leave supplicating for that person in your prayers so that the Lord can reward that person abundantly and give that person an excellent station. So, now my daughter is constantly praying for you that God does well with you the way you did good with her.

In regards to the letter which you had sent to Arman in the beginning of last month, indeed he did not get it until today. This is because ever since he had parted from you and travelled to Nice, he did not have the power to stay here but only for a few days. Then he departed to the west agonised and drowned in sorrow because of you. I did not know of his whereabouts or where he was staying. Thus, I was unable to post your letter to him until I learnt about his location only a few days earlier. I posted your letter to him along with a letter explaining your story. Indeed, in that letter I told him that certainly I did not see any reason preventing me giving him permission to travel to Paris and stay there for as long as you want him to. This is because now his sister is married. I am hoping that he will reach you very soon.

Today I am sending you this letter in conjunction with fifteen thousand Francs, hoping that you will accept them from me. I am hoping that you will look at this money like a daughter looks at a gift from her father who loves her and honours her. Thus, if you were to accept this gift you would be doing a very big favour upon me.

I am hoping that I will soon hear the news of your recovery. Also, I am hoping that I will see your health blossoming and your heart relishing in happiness.

Duval.

The moment I read that letter, I felt a wave of happiness running through me, which I only felt when I was with you. Certainly, I know now that Susan is married and this is what I had been hoping for. Indeed, you have always loved me. Verily I feared you forgetting me more than I feared your anger. Indeed, soon I shall see you and this is the only desire of my life.

Verily that gift which your father had sent me, certainly I did look at it with the eye that he had expected me to look with. Thus, I had accepted it thanking and praising him. May God favour him the way he has favoured me.

***

3rd February 1851

I could sleep last night unlike other nights. This is because the happiness which your father's letter left in my heart has indeed made me carefree of everything including my pain. In the morning, my doctor told me that I was much better than I had been in the recent past. He further added that indeed the sun is shining and the atmosphere is moderate, so mount upon your carriage and go out to the parks for a short while, then come back.

Thus, I went to the Shanzelize Park. Hence, I saw the park which was blossoming with life and with beauty. I saw the people in the park laughing, happy and enjoying themselves with a blessing whose value they did not recognise the way a deprived woman like me could recognise. I did get extremely upset when I saw a lot of people whom I knew walk passed me and not recognise me. Although I did see one of them looking at me, indeed he passed by the side of my carriage looking at me with a surprised and a suspicious look.

Thus, I have found out that I have certainly changed a great deal. Indeed, my mirror does not lie to me whenever it tells me about my weakness, about my pale colour and about my disfigured face. Verily my mirror tells me the truth the way the people tell the truth.

Then I saw the sun, indeed it was hiding behind its veil and I returned home. Certainly that fear which was in my heart, causing me to be upset, had perished. In place of it, a new thought which was better than it was born. This was the thought of meeting you very soon. Soon after meeting you, my days of misfortunes will be over.

***

7th February 1851

I do not think that you will meet me O Arman. Verily my illness has reached its last stages. I have become a lady who does not find any peace either in standing, sitting, sleeping or being awake. The pains have spread through my entire body and into my joints. I feel like a heavy stone from amongst the stones is resting upon my chest which is preventing me from breathing and moving. Today I am unable to get out of bed and go to my desk. So, I instructed Prudence to bring the ink pot and my diary to my bed and I am now writing to you while I am in my bed. O Arman when am I going to see you so that I can say my farewells to you before I die?

***

10th February 1851

My hopes and my desires in life have become extremely weak. This is because death is drawing closer to me slowly but surely. O Arman you have not come to me until now. I am presuming that I shall die before seeing you. Indeed, the thought of death is scaring me a great deal. It is filling up my heart with terror and fright. I do not know how I am going to have the power to live alone in that dark frightening ditch where I will have no helper, neither will I have anyone to speak with. I did not enjoy life for long. My dreams and my hopes were all I was left with and I am now dying before I could see any of my hopes and dreams turn to reality. How sweet is life and how bitter is the separation from it? I did not obtain much from life. However, I still would not like to leave this world. Verily lucky are those people who live a very long life and then die leaving behind pious offspring or righteous deeds. Then these pious offspring or righteous deeds remain living for a very long time after that person's death. Whereas me, soon I will be dying in the youth of my life. My memory will also die the moment I die. It will be like I had never lived a life.

Woe be upon me over the sins I committed in my past life. Today I am paying the price for my sins and for my mistakes. Indeed, I had the power to be content with one morsel and one gulp of water. I did not require anything else besides this. Nevertheless, I was not content. Thus, here I am now, I cannot even chew one morsel of food. Neither can I swallow one gulp of water. I cannot find anyway to continue living regardless of which form life takes. So, am I going to leave this world as a stranger the way I had come into this world? At my death, will not even my closest be present? Is there not going to be even a friend to cry over me? Will my life come to an end just like that? Are my dreams and my hopes going to reach fruition before they perish? Woe, only if death gave me a little respite. Only if when death approaches me I could see you one last time and then die.

After this I, do not have any desire. Only this morning, I saw my doctor whispering something in the ear of my maid when he was leaving me. I asked Prudence what he had said but she changed the topic and did not say anything about it. I am only presuming that it was a dangerous word which he had whispered to her. I cannot see things clearly around me anymore. I am struggling to see the whiteness of the paper which is in my hand. Before today I was only vomiting blood, but now I am also vomiting small chunks of my lungs. Only if there was a glass of poison which I could drink which then would relieve me from this torment. Death is approaching me faster than this poison. O Lord show mercy and show your favour. You are the only one who knows the proportion of my pain and my suffering. Be merciful to me and make easy for me my affair. O my Lord, grant me one ease out of the two. I do not see anything. Neither can I recognise what I am saying. Perhaps these might be the last words which I am writing with my hands.

***

14th February 1851

Do not grieve over me too much after my death O Arman. It is sufficient for me that you remember me and do not forget me. Let me give you good news, verily God has accepted my prayer as He has put in my heart the seed of tranquillity and hope since yesterday. This has wiped out all terrors and whispers from my heart. I am now certain that He is pleased with me and has forgiven for me my sins. Now I do not fear death, neither do I fear its aftermath. I am not agonizing over my pain anymore. Thus, you will not grieve over the affair of my death when you will come to know about it. May you live in happiness between your people and between your family. May you always honour your father. Verily he is from amongst the best fathers. May you also always love your sister. Indeed, she is from amongst the pure ladies. I am entrusting you to do good with Prudence. Verily she is a lady with a pure heart. She has great sincerity for me and you. I fear that after I am gone, the world might destroy her.

Most certainly God has created for a spirit another spirit from amongst the spirits which are similar to it and it meets it. It gets happy when it meets it and it becomes upset when it parts from it. However, God has decreed that every spirit stays away from its counterpart spirit in the first life. Thus, this is the misfortune of this world. Nevertheless, the spirits join its counterpart spirit in the second life. Thus, this is the fortune of the hereafter.

So, if my happiness with you upon this earth has finished, then soon I will be waiting for that happiness, waiting for you upon the highest heavens.

(Here some words which were written in the state of commotion have been wiped out through Margaret's tears and nothing is legible except for the word, 'Goodbye.')

THE VICTIM

Prudence's Diary

Remaining diary accounts through the pen of Prudence.

13th February 1851

O sir, Margaret did not have the power to write to you more than what she has already written because the doctor has prevented her from moving around. Even if she wanted to write she was unable to do so.

O sir, do you remember that fragile and tender body? Indeed, today that soft and glittering body has become a pile of bones. It has become a statue.

May mercy descend upon you, verily everything has collapsed in Margaret's body other than her heart and her brain. If only they had stopped functioning as well with the other organs. This is because your memories and your thoughts are punishing her.

Whenever someone enters through the door of her room, she raises her head thinking that you had come. However, when that person draws near her and she sees then she closes her eyes to hide her tears which will flow regardless.

Certainly, now she does not even talk a lot. Thus, if she was to speak, her first words would be, 'Has not Arman come?' When I reply with, 'No,' she starts questioning about some other affair shifting her attention towards it, or she simply returns to her state of silence again.

Indeed, her doctor not visiting today has placed doubt and suspicion in her mind. Nevertheless, when I presented her with an excuse, she did not believe me. She said, "Now I have understood that word which the doctor had whispered to you yesterday." I became silent and I did not know what I could say.

***

14th February 1851

Today Margaret's voice became extremely weak and I could not understand her. Her eyesight also became very weak; she was looking at me but she could not see me. Verily she gestured to me many times to open the windows of her room, so she could breathe easily. The windows of her room were already open and fresh air was passing through but it did not reach her.

O sir, woe, only if I had the power to sell my life so that I could buy for her some breathes which she could then comfortably take in and out of her lungs, or if I could buy for her some moments of sleep which she could then comfortably take refuge in. This is because her breathing was hurting and punishing me very severely. Verily three days have passed and she has not slept even for a little while.

***

15th February 1851

After a long silence in which she had not spoken even one word, she opened her eyes and called me in a weak voice and said to me, "I would like a priest, bring him to me." I realized that verily she has become firm in knowing that soon she will die. I started crying. I cried as much as God wanted me to cry. Then I went to the priest. He hesitated when I mentioned the name of the lady whom I wanted him to go to. Then I begged and pleaded to him to come. I said to him, "O my dear father, certainly the sinners and the transgressors are the ones who are entitled to the mercy of God." Then after some persuasion he agreed to come with me.

When he came, he spent some time alone in isolation with Margaret. After that he came out. I asked him, "Is God going to show mercy upon her O father?"

He said, "Indeed she has lived a very sinful life, however when she dies, she will die the death of the righteous." Thus, I thanked God for that.

Since that moment, I have not heard a single word from Margaret. Neither did I see any of her body parts moving. However, I did see that she was breathing in and out.

260

***

15th February 1851, evening time

Certainly, Margaret is in a lot of agony O master. I am presuming that she is undergoing the agony of death.

Now she is suffering so much pain. From time to time she screams so aggressively that her screams melt down the hearts.

Verily there came a moment in which her pain increased, she stood up screaming. She was standing on her bed. Then she opened her eyes and two big tears left her eyes. She sensed my presence and hugged me. She pressed herself against me tightly. She continued to hug me until her arms became tired and she returned to her state of agony.

***

15th February 1851, midnight

The matter passed and Margaret died. There was nothing remaining on her bed other than her corpse which would be taken to its grave tomorrow. This was her end consequence and the end of every living being. One can only be patient upon life's tribulations and on the decree of God.

Indeed, in the last moments of life, she yelled out your name many times O master. Her last action in her worldly life was that she looked at me for a very long time full of sorrows. Then she pointed with her finger towards her diary next to her and she said, "Arman." I understood that indeed she was entrusting me with it; that I ensure the diary reaches you. Then she entrusted her soul to God the Almighty.

O my dear lady Margaret, the punishment which you received before your death, has been very severe upon me. Your death has been very hard upon me. I did not find next to you anyone who could close your eyes and put a sheet of blanket over you other than myself. This pure and honourable soul has departed in the way of God that never troubled anyone, friend or foe. That spacious chest which could encompass the entire world including the earth and the heavens never became tight nor felt straitened for anyone. That clean and pure heart contained nothing other than good and hospitality. Nothing came out from her heart other than mercy and kindness.

***

Prudence cried next to the dead body of her lady as much as she could cry. Then she lit up candles besides her and called for the priest. The priest came, bowing down near Margaret's head, he started reciting something from his book. During this, Prudence walked towards the desk where she sat down and wrote the last account in her dairy. She continued to write until she was finished. Then she got up from her place frightened as she saw a shadow hovering upon the door of the room. Thus, she walked towards it only to discover that it was Arman dressed in white.

Indeed, when Arman walked in and cast his sight upon the location of the bed where the deceased was, he had a fit. Arman rolled his eyes back and accordingly he started staring at her again and asked, "Who is this person who is bowing down over her bed?" Thus, Prudence cried and did not say anything. Thus, Arman's bag fell from his hand, he became still neither talking nor moving.

Then, Arman rushed quickly towards the bed screaming. He wanted to throw himself upon the bed as well but Prudence held him and the priest stood in front of him. The priest said to him, "O young man, have some respect for the dead." Arman's tears remained buried within his chest and he was completely traumatised. In this state, he fell, unconscious. He did not regain consciousness until the sun had risen. That was the time when he realised that some people had come to take away the corpse. He stood up and collecting himself together, drew closer to the bed.

Arman said, "O people have mercy upon me, verily I lost the opportunity to say goodbye to her when she was alive, give me some respite now so that I can say my farewells to her in her death." The people felt mercy for him and created some space for him as Arman then drew closer to her. Arman lifted the veil from her face and kissed her forehead. Arman then said, "Goodbye O most honourable lady to me, goodbye O best lady on the earth and the most dignified soul of the heavens." Then he covered her face with that veil and moved back granting them the permission to take her away.

Arman walked behind her dead body crying and wailing. There were only three people walking behind the dead body, Arman, her maid Prudence and Duke Mohan. Duke Mohan was walking and reclining upon his walking stick and saying while crying and sobbing, "Today, I can see that my daughter has died in front of me once again and I am still living in the prison of life." Some women were also present at the funeral.

The day had not passed completely but everything else came to an end. Margaret was placed in her grave and Arman became ill and bed bound. He was reading Margaret's diary and crying incessantly, like one cries when he loses his beloved.

Then after this, Arman's illness increased. Thus, Prudence did not see any other alternative but to write to his father explaining the state of his son. Accordingly, his father, his sister Susan and Susan's husband came. They stayed with Arman for a month counselling him and treating his illness until he recovered and was completely out of danger.

Then all of them went together to the grave of Margaret to bid her farewell before travelling back. They all cried besides her grave. However, Susan's sobbing was the most painful, she did not know that the lady she was crying over was the one who has sacrificed her life for her.

Then Mr Duval approached his son and said to him, "O my son, do you forgive me my sin?"

Arman replied, "Yes I do O dear father because Margaret had already forgiven you." Then they all departed.

***

Many days and many years had passed. Mr Duval had passed away and his son had succeeded in his life just the way his father had wanted. However, their remained a wound in Arman's heart which never allowed him to be at peace whenever it inflamed. So, to attain some contentment he would read Margaret's diary, he would talk and hear about Margaret from Prudence, and he would visit Margaret's grave from time to time.

The End

References

Books

1. Mustafa, L (2006). *Al-Abarat (Arabic)*. Beirut, Lebanon: Ad-Daru-n-Namudhijiyyah. Pages 7-197.

2. Kokar, A & Akhyarullah, M (Date of Publication unknown). *Al-Abarat (Arabic - Urdu)*. Lahore, Pakistan: Maktaba Daniyal. Pages 4-381.

3. Rohi, B Dr. (2002). *Al-Mawrid - A Modern Arabic - English Dictionary*. 16th ed. Beirut, Lebanon: Dar El-Elm Lilmalayin. Pages 7-1255.

4. Ahmad Qureshi, B Prof. (1994). *Practical Twentieth Century Dictionary Urdu into English*. Delhi, India: Farid Book Depot (PVT) Ltd. Pages 1-688.

5. Hafeez Biyalvi, A (Translator) (2002). *Al-Munjad Arabic - Urdu*. Lahore, Pakistan: Maktaba Kadussiyah. Pages 29-1123.

Websites

1. Luebering, J.E. (2007). *Mustafa Lutfi al-Manfaluti Egyptian Author*. Available: https://www.britannica.com/biography/Mustafa-Lutfi-al-Manfaluti. Last accessed 3th April 2016.

2. Joynal, A - Research Scholar, Department of Arabic, Assam University. (2013). *Contribution of Mustafa Lutfi al-Manfaluti to Arabic Short Story: A Brief Study*. Available: http://www.iosrjournals.org/iosr-jhss/papers/Vol10-issue3/G01033437.pdf. Last accessed 12th April 2016.

13-08-19

Dearest Aasiya

Kush Ro
Stay Happy,

Jeeteh Ro
Stay Winning

Huste Ro
Stay laughing

Something my Aunty said to me once, her
words stuck with me,

H.W.